# LARVAE OF THE BRITISH EPHEMEROPTERA: A KEY WITH ECOLOGICAL NOTES

by

J. M. ELLIOTT
*Freshwater Biological Association*

U. H. HUMPESCH
*Limnological Institute, Austrian Academy of Sciences*

and

T. T. MACAN

*Illustrated by*

Prof. M. Mizzaro-Wimmer
*Zoological Institute, University of Vienna*

and

T. T. Macan

*FRESHWATER BIOLOGICAL ASSOCIATION*

*SCIENTIFIC PUBLICATION No. 49*

*1988*

Published by the Freshwater Biological Association, The Ferry House,
Ambleside, Cumbria LA22 0LP


ISBN 0 900386 47 9
ISSN 0367-1887

# PREFACE

The Association's first key to British Ephemeroptera, written by Mr D. E. Kimmins, was published in 1942 and included keys to the families and genera of larvae. These were omitted when a new key to adults was produced, and a separate key to larvae, written by Dr T. T. Macan, was published in 1961, with second and third editions in 1970 and 1979. Unfortunately, Dr Macan died on the 12th of January 1985 soon after he had commenced work on a new edition.

Some of the excellent illustrations from the earlier keys are included in the present publication but more have been added by Professor Mizzaro-Wimmer, and the text has been completely rewritten by Drs Elliott and Humpesch. These authors have included many of their own excellent researches in the expanded section on ecology.

Larvae of Ephemeroptera are important not only as a food for fish but also as indicators of water quality. As the second half of this book describes, the Ephemeroptera have different life-histories and habits that are of interest to both entomologists and freshwater biologists. I hope that all will welcome this publication in the Association's series.

The Ferry House
February 1988

J. G. Jones
*Director*

# CONTENTS

# INTRODUCTION

Ephemeroptera belong to the Exopterygota (or Hemimetabola), i.e. those insects with an incomplete metamorphosis, with a larva that basically resembles the adult in appearance, with wings that develop externally as wing buds in the immature stages, and with a life cycle divided into three definite stages of egg, larva and adult. The name Ephemeroptera (Greek *ephemeros* = lasting for a day; *pteron* = wing) refers to the brief life of the adult which is sometimes called a 'mayfly' or 'one-day fly'. Ephemeroptera are unique among winged insects in having two adult stages. The first, called the *subimago*, emerges from the last larval stage and, depending on air temperature, usually moults within 24 hours to the second, called the *imago* (plural *imagines*). Fishermen usually refer to the subimago as the dun and the imago as the spinner. There is some disagreement about the terminology of the immature stages. The term *larvae* is used in this text but other workers use the terms nymph, nymphules and naiads.

The key to larvae in the present publication is partially based on the earlier key by Macan (1979). A key to adults of the British species and a detailed review of adult ecology can be found in Elliott & Humpesch (1983). The general biology of Ephemeroptera was reviewed by Illies (1968) and more recent literature has been reviewed by Brittain (1982). Information on the life cycles of 297 species has been summarised by Clifford (1982).

## GENERAL CHARACTERS

The basic external structure of the larva is illustrated in fig. 1.

*Head.* The shape varies between genera but there are always large compound eyes situated laterally or dorsally, and usually one median and two lateral *ocelli* situated between the eyes. The slender tapering *antennae* vary in length between genera. The mouth parts vary according to feeding habits but consist of four main elements. A *labrum* is the most anterior mouthpart and is a flap that can move slightly backwards and forwards. A pair of jaw-like *mandibles*, each with outer incisors and an inner molar region, lie posterior to the labrum and move laterally to provide a chewing action. In the genus *Baetis*, the mandibles have an unusual appendage known as a *prostheca*. Posterior to the mandibles is another pair of chewing organs, the *maxillae*, each of which carries a segmented *palp* (usually three segments, sometimes two to four). The *labium* is the most posterior mouthpart and bears a pair of palps and two pairs of lobes, the inner pair being the *glossae* and the outer pair the *paraglossae*.

*Thorax and legs.* There are three thoracic segments: anterior *prothorax* with the fore legs, *mesothorax* with the middle pair of legs and the developing fore wings in older larvae, posterior *metathorax* with the hind-legs and developing hind wings, except in those species whose adults lack hind wings. The dorsal surfaces of the three segments are known as the *pronotum, mesonotum* and *metanotum*, the largest always being the mesonotum which usually covers the metanotum. Each leg has six parts: a stout basal *coxa*, a small *trochanter*, a broad *femur*, a slender cylindrical or subtriangular *tibia*, a cylindrical unsegmented *tarsus*, and a single *claw* often with small 'teeth' (denticles).

*Abdomen and gills.* There are ten abdominal segments, some of which may be hidden beneath the mesonotum. Each segment has a dorsal *tergum* (or *tergite*) and a ventral *sternum* (or *sternite*). To determine the number of a segment, always count forward from the tenth posterior segment. The so-called 'gills' occur on up to seven abdominal segments (numbers 1-7) but are less numerous in some species. At the posterior end of the abdomen, two *cerci* and a median *terminal filament* form the three *caudal filaments* or '*tails*' (all the British species have three tails but some species outside the British Isles do not have the median filament). Unlike that of the adults, the body shape of the larvae often varies considerably between families (figs. 3, 4, 5).

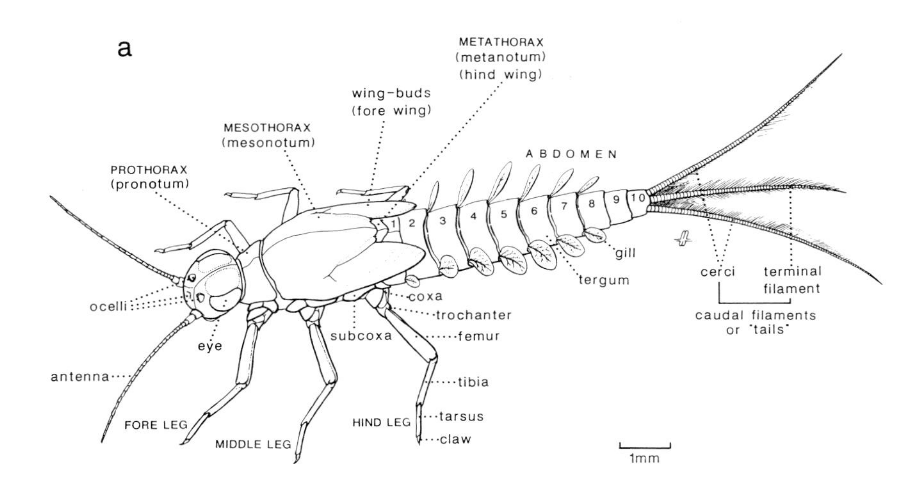


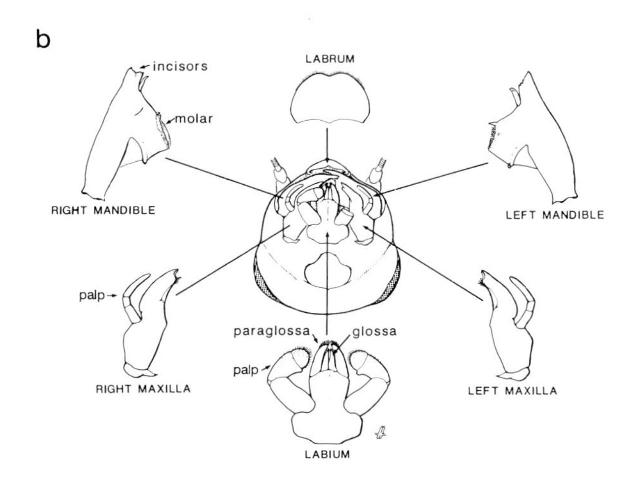


Fig. 1. *a*, Basic structure of a larva (scale line 1 mm); *b*, ventral view of mouthparts (original drawings by M. Mizzaro).

## CLASSIFICATION AND CHECK LIST

Historical changes in the classification of Ephemeroptera were briefly reviewed by Elliott & Humpesch (1983). The system used in the present publication is that proposed by McCafferty & Edmunds (1979) who divided the order into two fundamental suborders. In the suborder Schistonota (split-back mayflies), the larvae have developing forewing pads that are free for at least half of their length beyond their fusion to the thorax. There are usually well-developed gills along the abdomen and the larvae are active. In the suborder Pannota (fused-back mayflies), less than half of the forewing pads extends freely beyond their fusion to the thorax. The gills tend to be reduced and protected in various ways, and the larvae are usually sluggish until just before emergence of the subimagines. For the extant Ephemeroptera, three superfamilies and thirteen families are placed in the Schistonota, and three superfamilies and six families are placed in the Pannota. Eight families occur in the British Isles, six in the Schistonota (Siphlonuridae, Baetidae, Heptageniidae, Leptophlebiidae, Potamanthidae, Ephemeridae) and two in the Pannota (Ephemerellidae, Caenidae). Eighteen genera and forty-eight species are included in the check list (Table 1).

The monograph by Müller-Liebenau (1969) was used for the nomenclature in the genus *Baetis*. The species previously identified as *B. bioculatus* (L.) has been found to be *B. fuscatus*, and the true *bioculatus* belongs to another genus. *B. tenax* Eaton is now regarded as a synonym of *B. vernus*, but it may prove to be a valid species. Macan (1979) suggests that there is an ecological distinction; *tenax* is found in the upper reaches of small stony streams rising at high altitudes in the mountains of Britain whereas *vernus* is found in slow-flowing weedy rivers. *B. pumilus* (Burmeister) is now a synonym of *B. muticus*. Sowa (1975a) suggests that the name *Cloeon dipterum* covers more than one species but Macan (1979) provides reasons why the name should still be retained for British specimens. It is now accepted that *Siphlonurus linnaeanus* (Eaton) is a synonym of *S. alternatus* (Jacob 1974a; Puthz 1977; Malzacher 1981), *Procloeon pseudorufulum* Kimmins and *P. rufulum* Eaton are synonyms of *P. bifidum* (Sowa 1975b), *Rhithrogena haarupi* Esben-Petersen is a synonym of *R. germanica* (Sowa 1971), *Paraleptophlebia tumida* Bengtsson is a synonym of *P. werneri* (Landa 1969; Puthz 1978), and *Caenis moesta* Bengtsson is a synonym of *C. luctuosa* (Jacob 1974b; Malzacher 1984, 1986). An additional species, *Caenis pusilla*, has recently been recorded in Britain (Malzacher 1986). *Heptagenia lateralis* has not been transferred to the genus *Ecdyonurus*, as proposed by some workers (e.g. Bogoescu & Tabacaru 1962; Puthz 1978).

TABLE 1. A CHECK-LIST OF THE BRITISH EPHEMEROPTERA

| Family | Genus | Species | |
|---|---|---|---|
| SIPHLONURIDAE | SIPHLONURUS Eaton, 1868 | *armatus* Eaton, 1870 | (1) |
| | | *lacustris* Eaton, 1870 | (2) |
| | | *alternatus* (Say, 1824) | (3) |
| | AMELETUS Eaton, 1885 | *inopinatus* Eaton, 1887 | (4) |
| BAETIDAE | BAETIS Leach, 1815 | *fuscatus* (Linnaeus, 1761) | (5) |
| | | *scambus* Eaton, 1870 | (6) |
| | | *vernus* Curtis, 1834 | (7) |
| | | *buceratus* Eaton, 1870 | (8) |
| | | *rhodani* (Pictet, 1844) | (9) |
| | | *atrebatinus* Eaton, 1870 | (10) |
| | | *muticus* (Linnaeus, 1758) | (11) |
| | | *niger* (Linnaeus, 1761) | (12) |
| | | *digitatus* Bengtsson, 1912 | (13) |
| | CENTROPTILUM Eaton, 1869 | *luteolum* (Müller, 1776) | (14) |
| | | *pennulatum* Eaton, 1870 | (15) |
| | CLOEON Leach, 1815 | *dipterum* (Linnaeus, 1761) | (16) |
| | | *simile* Eaton, 1870 | (17) |
| | PROCLOEON Bengtsson, 1915 | *bifidum* (Bengtsson, 1912) | (18) |
| HEPTAGENIIDAE | RHITHROGENA Eaton, 1881 | *semicolorata* (Curtis, 1834) | (19) |
| | | *germanica* Eaton, 1885 | (20) |
| | HEPTAGENIA Walsh, 1863 | *sulphurea* (Müller, 1776) | (21) |
| | | *longicauda* (Stephens, 1835) | (22) |
| | | *fuscogrisea* (Retzius, 1783) | (23) |
| | | *lateralis* (Curtis, 1834) | (24) |
| | ARTHROPLEA Bengtsson, 1909 | *congener* Bengtsson, 1909 | (25) |
| | ECDYONURUS Eaton, 1868 | *venosus* (Fabricius, 1775) | (26) |
| | | *torrentis* Kimmins, 1942) | (27) |
| | | *dispar* (Curtis, 1834) | (28) |
| | | *insignis* (Eaton, 1870) | (29) |
| LEPTOPHLEBIIDAE | LEPTOPHLEBIA Westwood, 1840 | *marginata* (Linnaeus, 1767) | (30) |
| | | *vespertina* (Linnaeus, 1758) | (31) |
| | PARALEPTOPHLEBIA Lestage, 1917 | *submarginata* (Stephens, 1835) | (32) |
| | | *cincta* (Retzius, 1783) | (33) |
| | | *werneri* Ulmer, 1919 | (34) |
| | HABROPHLEBIA Eaton, 1881 | *fusca* (Curtis, 1834) | (35) |
| POTAMANTHIDAE | POTAMANTHUS Pictet, 1843-5 | *luteus* (Linnaeus, 1767) | (36) |
| EPHEMERIDAE | EPHEMERA Linnaeus, 1758 | *vulgata* Linnaeus, 1758 | (37) |
| | | *danica* Müller, 1764 | (38) |
| | | *lineata* Eaton, 1870 | (39) |
| EPHEMERELLIDAE | EPHEMERELLA Walsh, 1862 | *ignita* (Poda, 1761) | (40) |
| | | *notata* Eaton, 1887 | (41) |
| CAENIDAE | BRACHYCERCUS Curtis, 1834 | *harrisella* Curtis, 1834 | (42) |
| | CAENIS Stephens, 1835 | *macrura* Stephens, 1835 | (43) |
| | | *luctuosa* (Burmeister, 1839) | (44) |
| | | *robusta* Eaton, 1884 | (45) |
| | | *horaria* (Linnaeus, 1758) | (46) |
| | | *rivulorum* Eaton, 1884 | (47) |
| | | *pusilla* Navas, 1913 | (48) |

## COLLECTION AND PRESERVATION

Larvae can be collected from shallow water with a pond net which can be swept through vegetation or thrust beneath stones as these are lifted from the bottom. Collecting in deeper water is more difficult but numerous grabs, dredges, corers and air-lift samplers have been used for qualitative and quantitative sampling of benthic macroinvertebrates, including larvae of Ephemeroptera (see annotated bibliographies of Elliott & Tullett, 1978, 1983).

Whenever possible, live larvae should be brought back to the laboratory because their general appearance, especially the angle at which their tails are held, and their general behaviour, especially swimming ability, make many species easier to identify alive than dead. To prevent damage to the larvae, they should be separated in the field from stones and carnivores taken in the samples. The larger the volume of water in which the larvae are transported, the greater their chances of survival, as a large volume warms more slowly and contains more oxygen. Alternatively the larvae can be transported in a gauze cage fitted within a thermos flask containing a mixture of ice and water.

Adults can be bred from mature larvae that have characteristic black wing-pads. They are reared in a cage in a stream or in an aerated aquarium. The advantage of this method is that it yields not only an imago but also a series of larval skins and a subimago belonging to a known adult. Such a series is often useful for other taxonomic studies, especially when different morphological and biochemical characters are used. Moreover, small spines and scales are seen more easily on cast skins than on whole larvae, and therefore when identification depends on these features, it is easier if the larvae can be kept alive until they have moulted.

Larvae should be preserved in fluid, e.g. 70% alcohol, dilute formaldehyde (one part of 40% formaldehyde to nineteen parts of water), or a mixture of alcohol and dilute formaldehyde, and kept in the dark so that they do not rapidly lose their colour. If formaldehyde is used, then the specimen should be first wetted in 70% alcohol. Another suitable fixative fluid is Pämpel's mixture (four parts of glacial acetic acid, thirty parts of distilled water, six parts of 40% formaldehyde and fifteen parts of 96% alcohol). An excellent killing fluid and preservative for material suitable for dissection is K.A.A.D. (one part of kerosene, ten parts of 95% alcohol, two parts of glacial acetic acid, one part of dioxan). All specimens should have a label written in waterproof ink, and the label should give the place of collection, preferably as a National Grid Reference, as well as the collector's name, the species name when known and the full date of collection.

# KEY TO FAMILIES

Larvae of British Ephemeroptera can be separated from larvae of other aquatic insects by the following set of characters (see fig. 1): compound eyes, one claw on each leg, only abdominal gills (hidden under a large pair of gill covers in the family Caenidae), two pairs of wing pads in older larvae, and three 'tails' (some species found outside the British Isles have only two 'tails'). The British species belong to eight families that can be separated chiefly on the form of the abdominal gills and also on their general appearance (see figs 2, 3, 4, 5).

1 First pair of gills reduced to tapering filaments; other gills stacked under large pair of gill covers (formed from second pair of gills) (figs 2, 3*a*). Larvae found in mud and vegetable debris in still and flowing water— CAENIDAE, p. 72

— Most gills visible— **2**

2 Gills feathery, consisting of two branches each thickly fringed with filaments (figs 2, 3*b*, *c*)— **3**

— Gills not feathery, consisting of one plate, two plates, one large plate and a tuft of filaments, or one small plate and up to twelve filaments (fig. 2)— **4**

3 Gills held over back during life; mandibles project well beyond front of head (figs 2, 3*b*). Larvae burrow in gravel, sand or mud in still and flowing water— EPHEMERIDAE, p. 68

— Gills extending out sideways from body during life; mandibles do not project beyond front of head (figs 2, 3*c*). Larvae found chiefly in large rivers, often in side pools with a bottom of stones and sand— POTAMANTHIDAE, p. 68

4(2) Body strongly flattened dorso-ventrally with very broad head, thorax and femora of legs; eyes placed dorsally; seven pairs of gills, each consisting of a flat plate and usually a separate tuft of filaments (the tuft is absent from the last pair of gills in some species and from all gills in *Arthroplea congener* which is distinguished immediately by its unique maxillary palp, and probably does not occur in the British Isles; there is only one doubtful record from Stanmore, Middlesex in 1920) (figs 2, 3*d*, 4*a*). Larvae cling to stones and boulders on lake shores, and in streams and rivers— HEPTAGENIIDAE, p. 50

— Body not flattened and without broad head and thorax; eyes placed laterally; gills never consisting of a flat plate and a separate tuft of filaments— **5**

5 Four pairs of plate-like gills visible (the 5th pair is small and hidden beneath the 4th), and held dorsally over the abdomen so that when the larva is viewed from above, the gills do not project beyond the sides of the body; tails with short scattered bristles (figs 2, 4*b*). Larvae are poor swimmers and are usually found under stones or amongst bryophytes and macrophytes in streams, rivers and occasionally in lakes— EPHEMERELLIDAE, p. 70

— Six or seven pairs of gills that clearly project beyond the sides of the abdomen when the larva is viewed from above— **6**

6 Each gill consisting of either two strap-like filaments, or a plate that tapers to a single filament, or a small base that supports several filaments; tails as long as or longer than the body; each tail with short, sparse hairs on both sides (figs 2, 4*c*). Larvae crawl on the substratum or swim in a laboured fashion and are found in ponds, lakes, streams and rivers— LEPTOPHLEBIIDAE, p. 62

— Each gill consisting of a single plate, or some, never more than six, may consist of two plates; tails never as long as the body; tails fringed with long close-set hairs on inside edge of outer tails and on both sides of middle tail (figs 2, 4*d*, 5). Larvae are good swimmers and are found in ponds, lakes, streams and rivers— **7**

7 Hind corners of penultimate segment of abdomen and two or three segments before it are drawn out to form spines; tails of similar length with a broad black band across their middle (figs 2, 4*d*) (spines are clearly seen in the genus *Siphlonurus* but are rather small in *Ameletus inopinatus* which may be wrongly identified as a member of the family Baetidae, see notes below). Larvae are good swimmers and are found in streams, rivers, ponds and lakes— SIPHLONURIDAE, p. 22

— Hind corners of abdominal segments not drawn out to form spines; tails either of similar length (*Cloeon*, *Procloeon*, *Centroptilum*) or middle tail shorter than the others (*Baetis*) (fig. 5). Larvae are good swimmers and are found in streams, rivers, ponds and lakes— BAETIDAE, p. 26

There may be problems in separating *Ameletus inopinatus* from the Baetidae. The plate-like gills are single and oval without a pointed tip in *Ameletus* and *Baetis* (fig. 2) but the two genera are easily separated by tail length, all tails equal in *Ameletus* and middle tail shorter than others in *Baetis* (e.g. figs 5*c*, *d*). Unlike the single gills of *Ameletus*, six of the seven gills of *Cloeon* (fig. 5*b*) and *Centroptilum pennulatum* are double plates with one plate larger than the other. *Ameletus inopinatus* may be confused with *Centroptilum luteolum* (fig. 5*a*) and *Procloeon bifidum* because all three species have tails of similar length and single gills. The latter are, however, without a pointed tip in *Ameletus*, with a pointed tip and shaped like a beech-leaf in *C. luteolum* and markedly asymmetrical in *P. bifidum* (fig. 9*d*, *e*). If still in doubt, it is worth removing the maxillae of *Ameletus* (see fig. 1*b* for position amongst mouth parts). Each maxilla has distinct comb-like bristles (fig. 6) that are similar to those found in the Heptageniidae but are never found in the Baetidae.

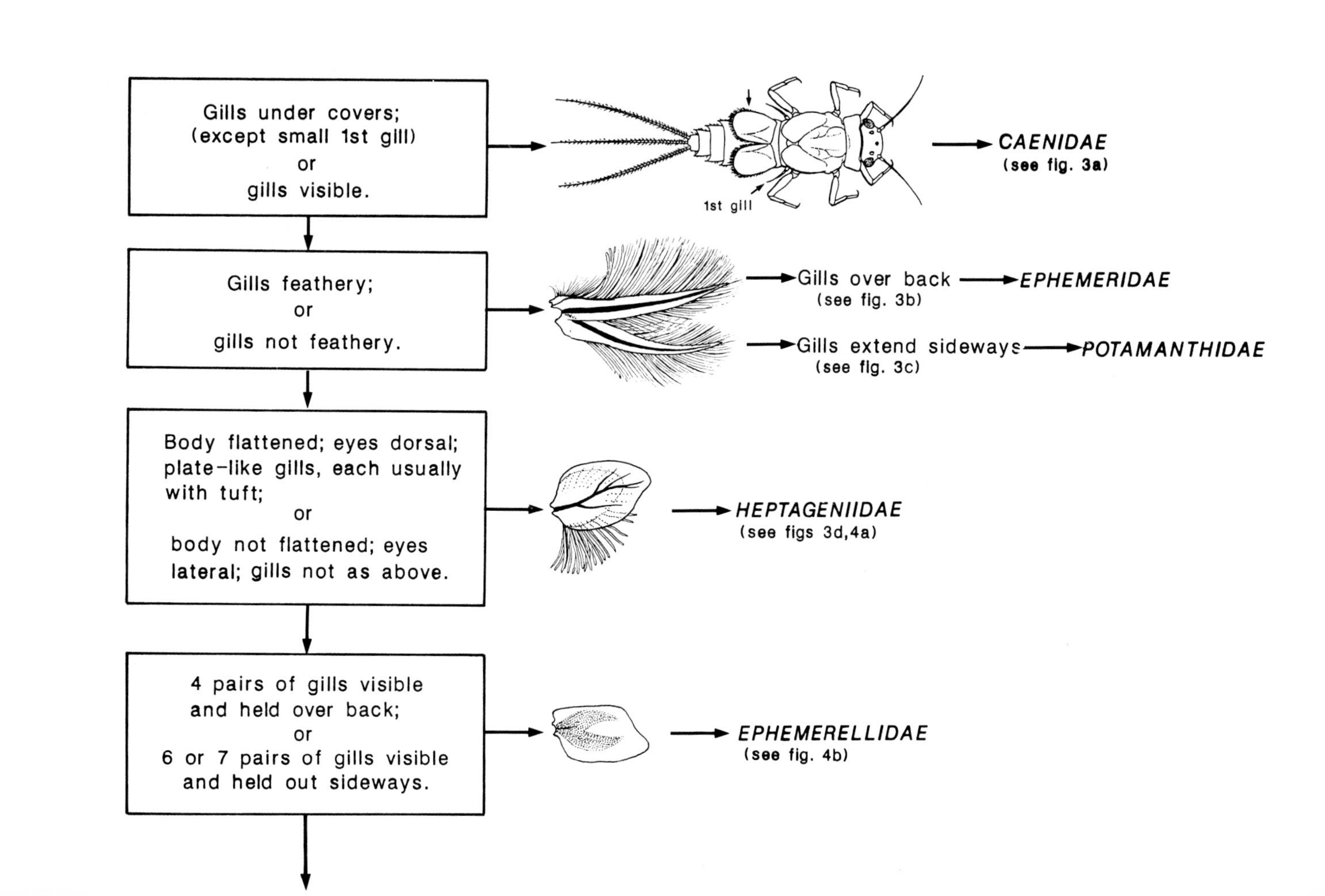
Gills under covers;
(except small 1st gill)
or
gills visible.
1st gill
CAENIDAE
(see fig. 3a)
Gills feathery;
or
gills not feathery.
Gills over back
(see fig. 3b)
EPHEMERIDAE
Gills extend sideways
(see fig. 3c)
POTAMANTHIDAE
Body flattened; eyes dorsal; plate-like gills, each usually with tuft;
or
body not flattened; eyes lateral; gills not as above.
HEPTAGENIIDAE
(see figs 3d,4a)
4 pairs of gills visible and held over back;
or
6 or 7 pairs of gills visible and held out sideways.
EPHEMERELLIDAE
(see fig. 4b)

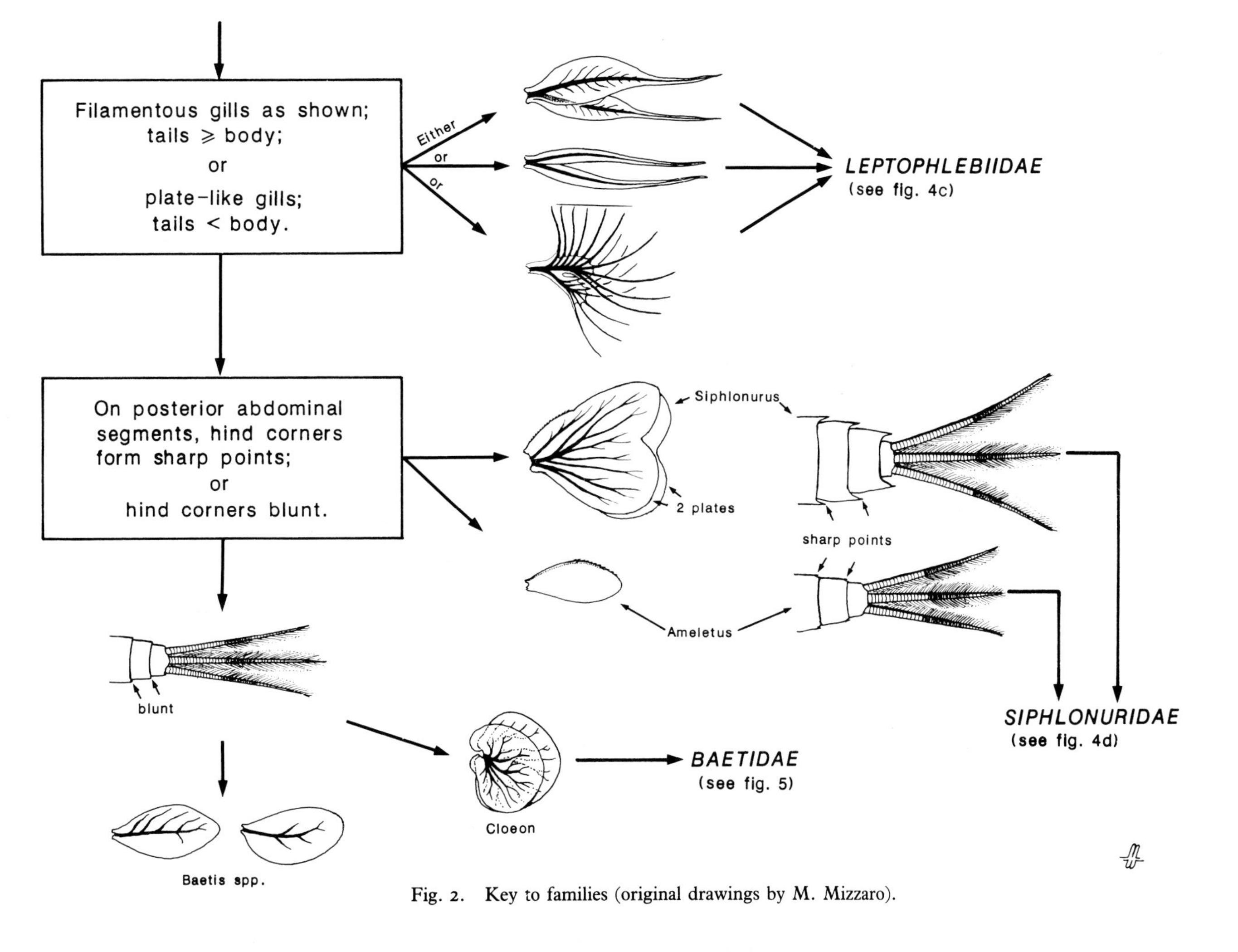


Fig. 2. Key to families (original drawings by M. Mizzaro).

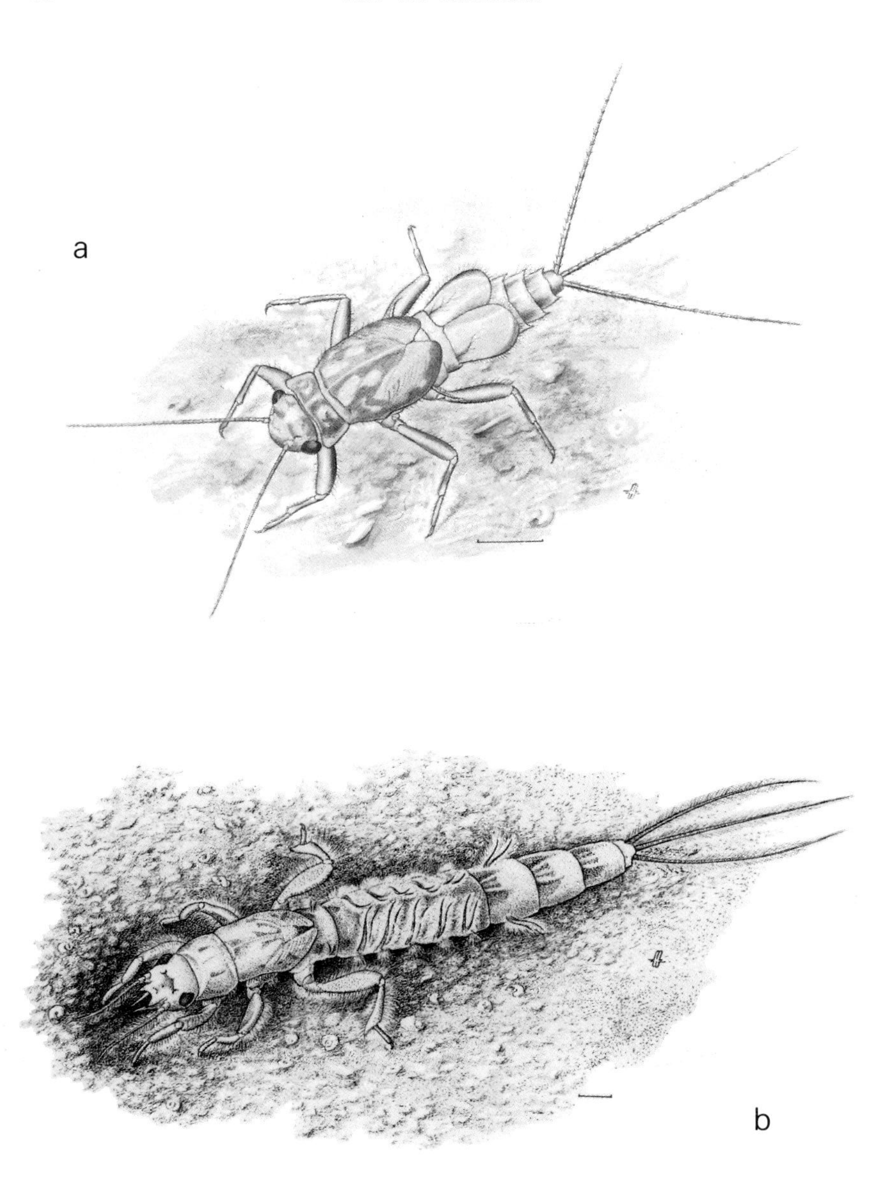


Fig. 3. Examples of larvae from families: *a*, Caenidae (*Caenis horaria*); *b*, Ephemeridae (*Ephemera danica*); *c*, Potamanthidae (*Potamanthus luteus*); *d*, Heptageniidae (*Rhithrogena* sp.). (Scale lines 1 mm; original drawings by M. Mizzaro).

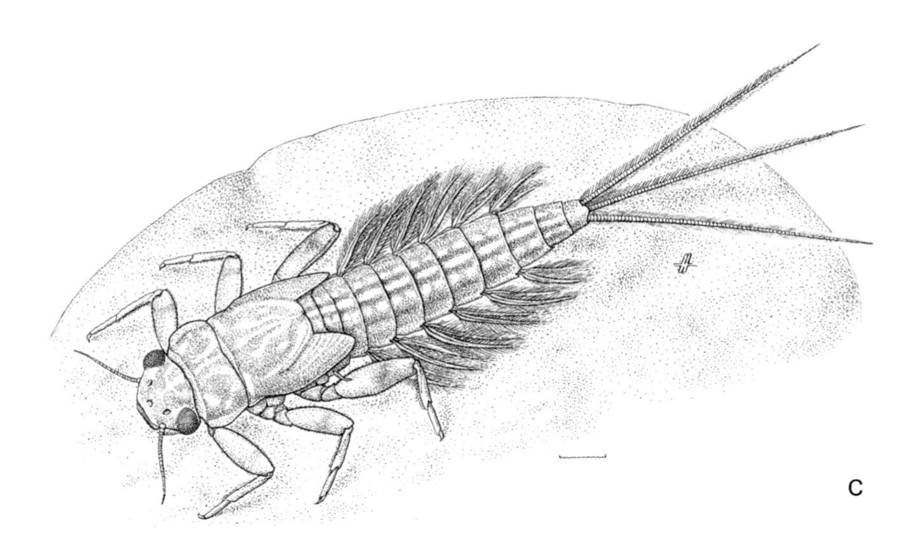
c

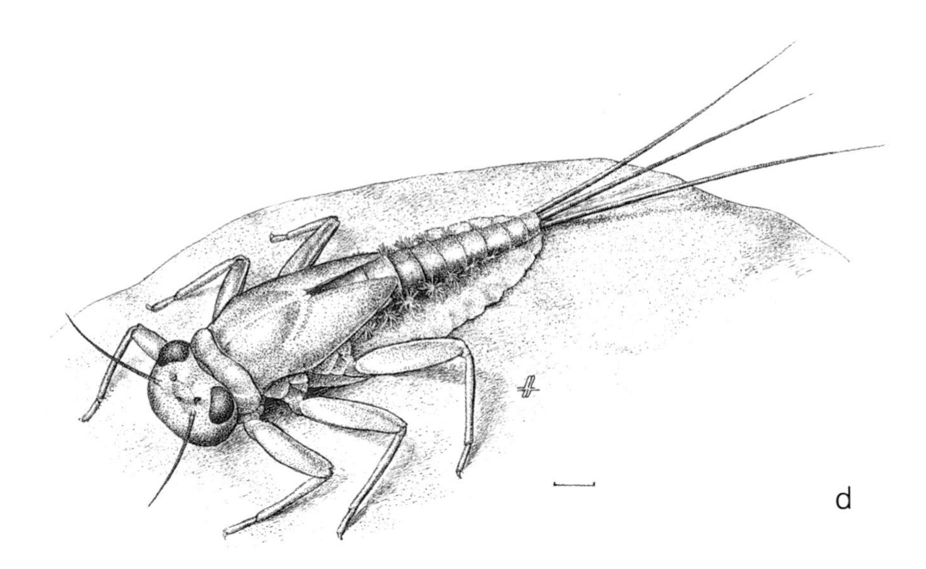
d

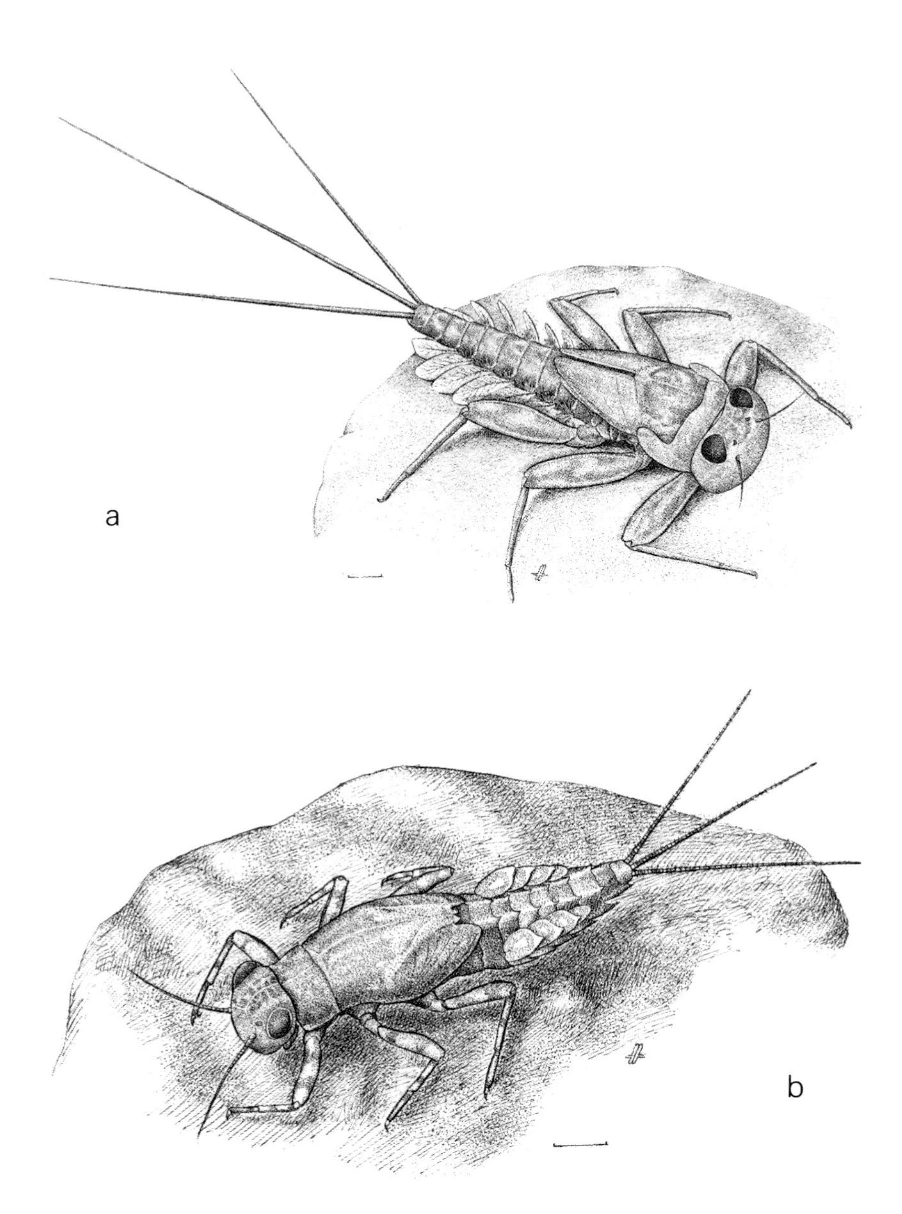
a
b

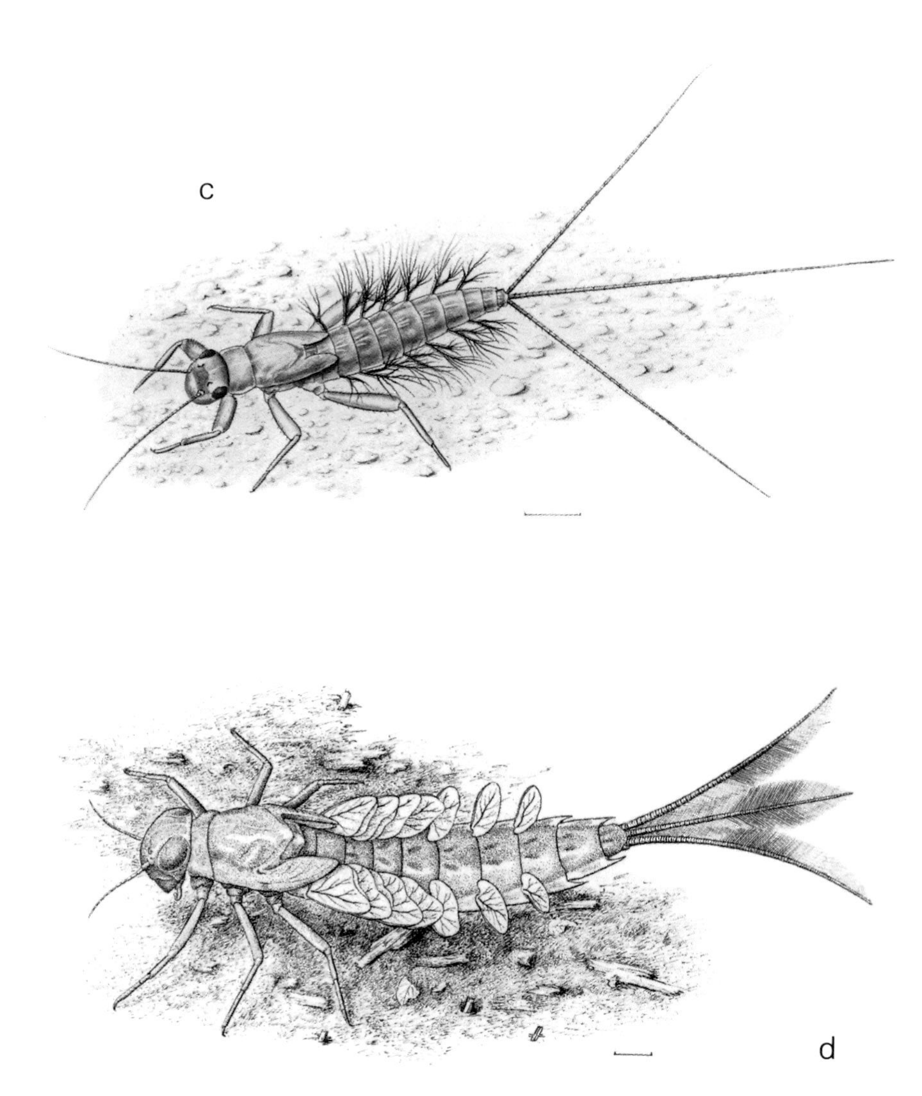


Fig. 4. Examples of larvae from families: *a*, Heptageniidae (*Ecdyonurus* sp.); *b*, Ephemerellidae (*Ephemerella ignita*); *c*, Leptophlebiidae (*Habrophlebia* sp.); *d*, Siphlonuridae (*Siphlonurus* sp.). (Scale lines 1 mm; original drawings by M. Mizzaro).

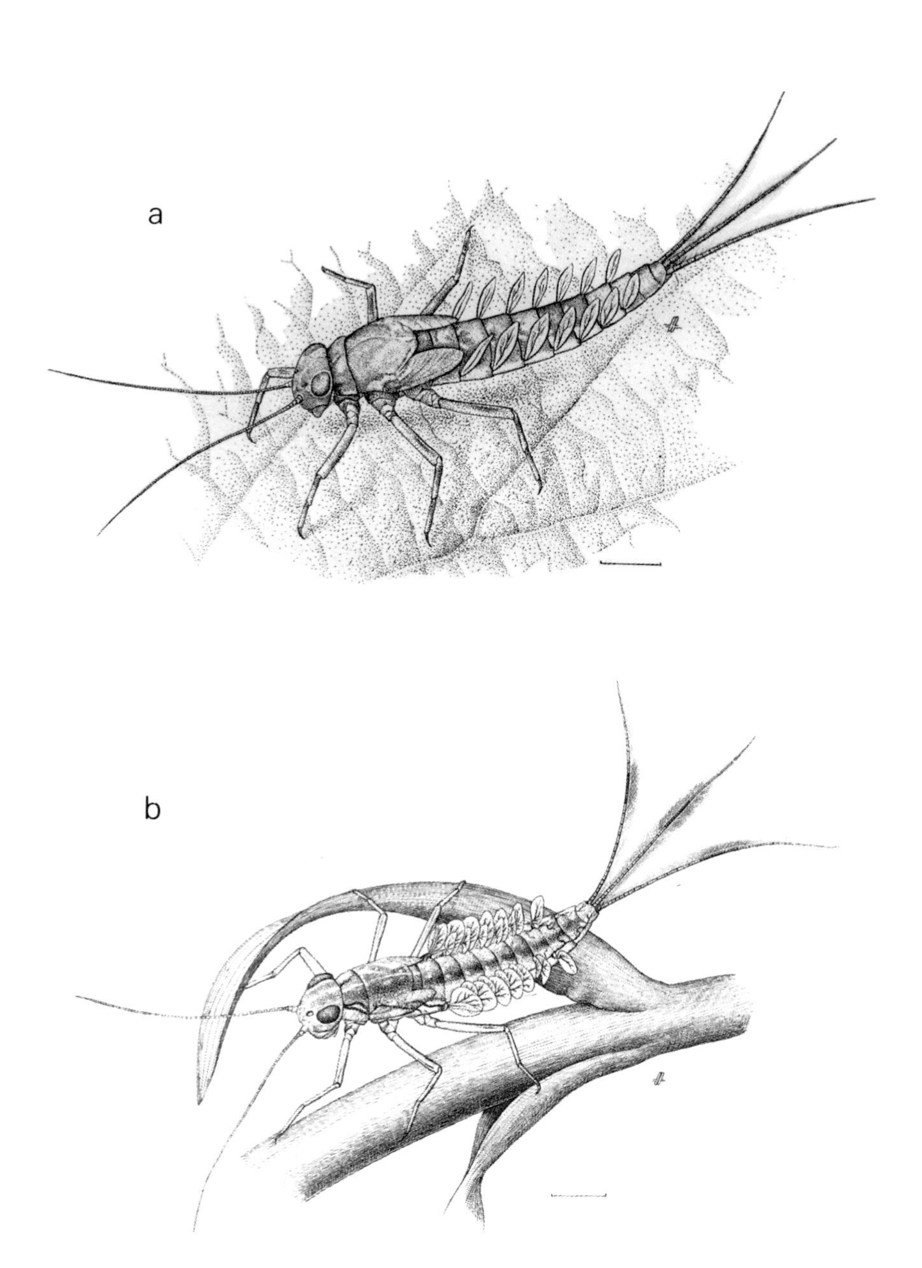
a
b

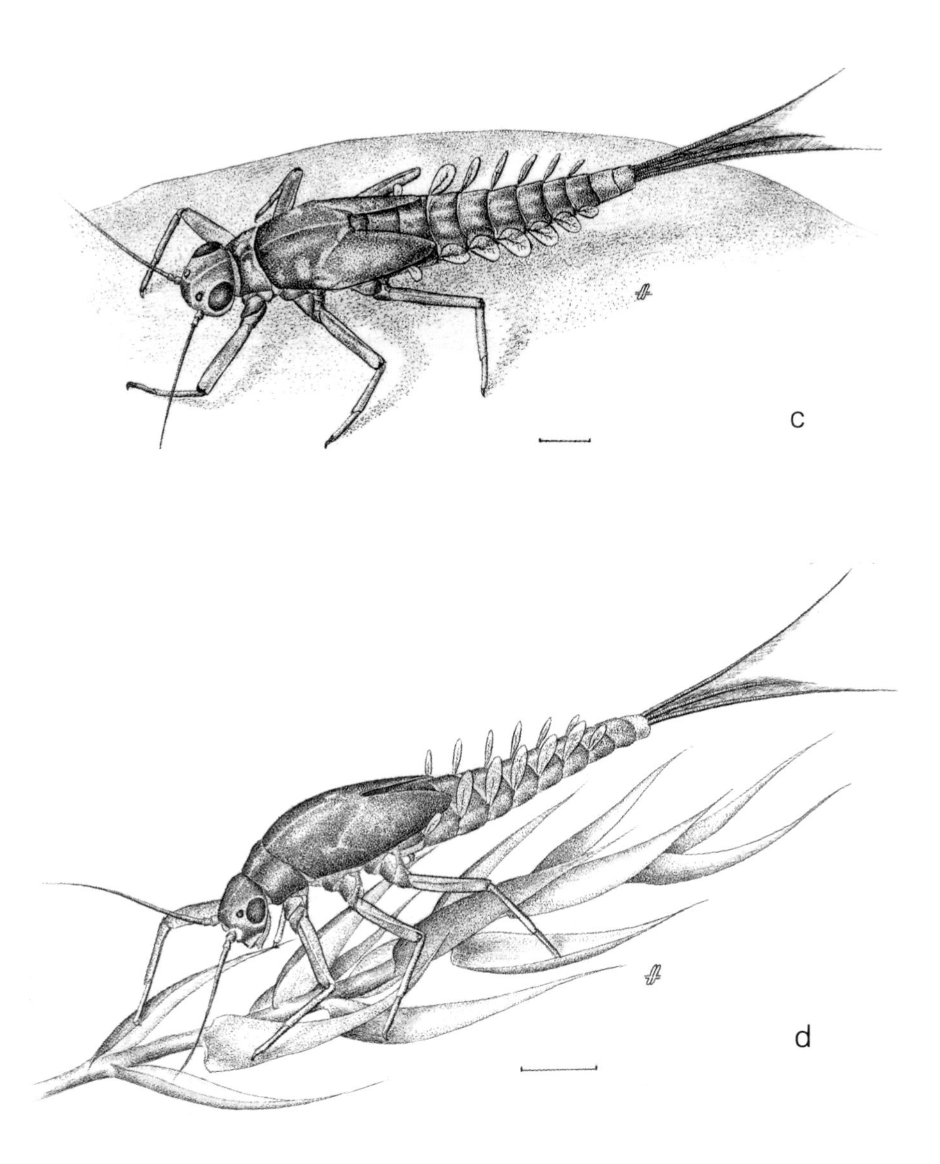


Fig. 5. Examples of larvae from family Baetidae: *a*, *Centroptilum luteolum*; *b*, *Cloeon dipterum*; *c*, *Baetis rhodani*; *d*, *B. muticus*. (Scale lines 1 mm; original drawings by M. Mizzaro).

# KEY TO SPECIES

## Family SIPHLONURIDAE

1 Spines formed by hind corners of abdominal segments are rather small (figs 6*b*, 8*j*), tails in live larva held close together (fig. 6*b*); maxillae with comb-like bristles (fig. 6*c*); seven pairs of gills, each gill single and oval (fig. 7*a*); larva up to 11 mm long—
**Ameletus inopinatus** Eaton

Larvae found chiefly in mountain streams but also recorded from several lochs in northwest Scotland.

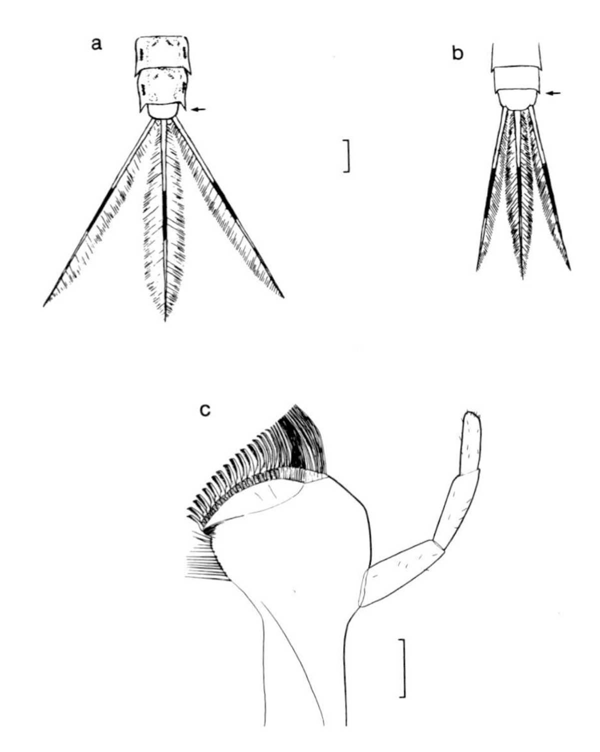


Fig. 6. Siphlonuridae: *a*, hind end of *Siphlonurus lacustris* from life; *b*, hind end of *Ameletus inopinatus* from life; *c*, maxilla of *A. inopinatus*. (Scale lines *a* and *b*, 1 mm; *c*, 0·2 mm).

— Spines formed by hind corners of abdominal segments are large and distinct (figs 6*a*, 8*g*, *h*, *i*), tails in live larva held apart (fig. 6*a*); maxillae without comb-like bristles (fig. 8*a*); seven pairs of gills, some of which are double plates and most of which are not oval (fig. 7*b*); larva up to 18 mm long— **2**

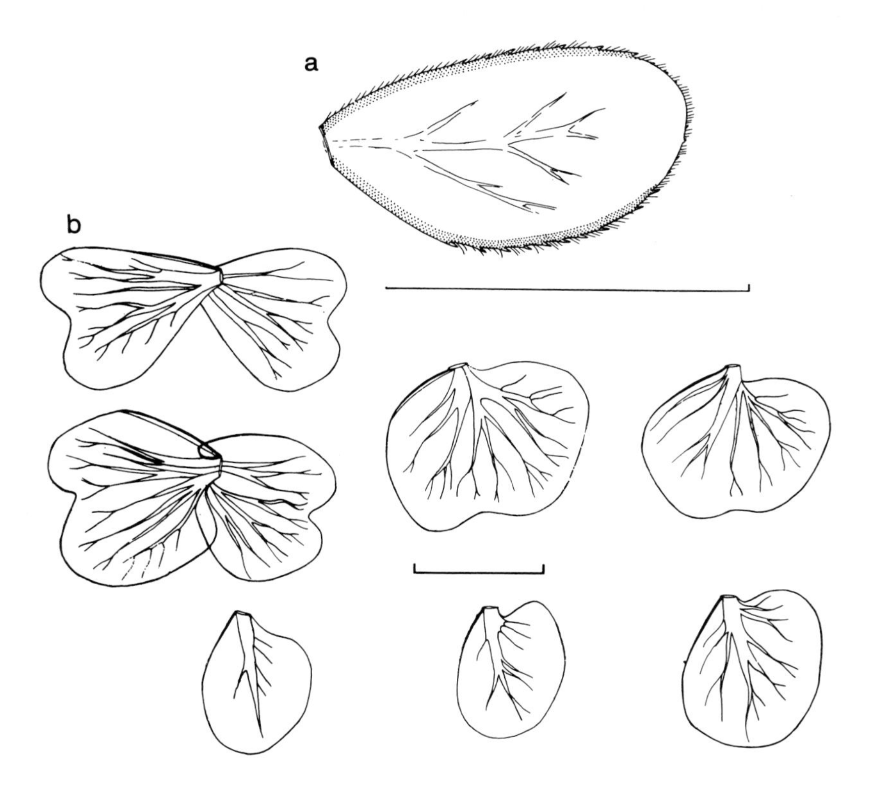


Fig. 7. Siphlonuridae: *a*, single gill of *Ameletus inopinatus*; *b*, set of gills from *Siphlonurus lacustris*. (Scale lines 1 mm).

2 First six gills are double plates, last gill single; each abdominal segment has a dark band running transversely from the central pigmented area of the tergum to the lateral margin (fig. 8*g*)—
**Siphlonurus alternatus** (Say)

Larvae found chiefly in calcareous lakes and deep pools in slow-flowing rivers.

— First two gills are double plates, remaining five gills single (fig. 7*b*); abdominal segments not marked as above (figs 8*h*, *i*)— **3**

3 One row of 4-7 bristles on the inner margin of the middle segment of the maxillary palp (fig. 8*c*) (these long bristles can be easily seen on the whole larva with the high power of a binocular microscope; there is also a second row of tiny bristles that are not easily seen and therefore appear to be absent; if you are not sure which is the maxillary palp, check with fig. 1*b*); on the upper surface of the last segment of the labial palp, the larger bristles are arranged in a group at the tip and a single row along the segment (fig. 8*f*) (this character is not easily seen on the whole larva but is more obvious on a detached labium; if you are not sure which is the labium, check with fig. 1*b*); spines formed by hind corners of abdominal segment 9 are short, reaching only about half-way down the sides of segment 10; round or oval dark marks on lateral margins of abdominal segments 8 and 9, and usually on 2-7 (fig. 8*i*)— **Siphlonurus lacustris** Eaton

Larvae found chiefly in lakes, slow-flowing sections of streams and rivers, and ponds at high altitudes.

— Two rows of long bristles with 8-12 bristles altogether on the inner margin of the middle segment of the maxillary palp (fig. 8*b*); on the upper margin of the last segment of the labial palp, larger bristles not arranged in single row along the segment (fig. 8*e*); spines formed by hind corners of abdominal segment 9 are long, nearly reaching to the tip of segment 10; no markings on lateral margins of abdominal segments except segments 8 and 9 that sometimes have elongate dark marks (fig. 8*h*)— **Siphlonurus armatus** Eaton

Larvae found chiefly in lakes, ponds and slow-flowing streams and rivers.

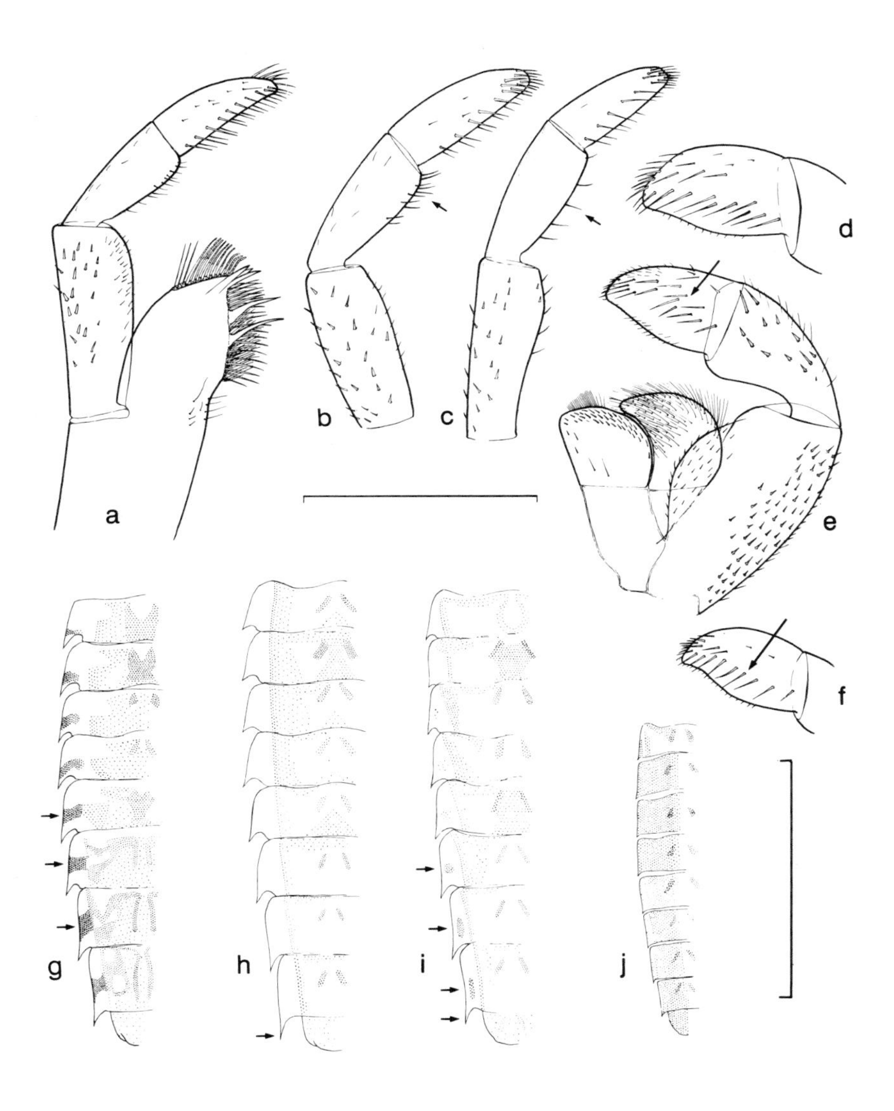


Fig. 8. Siphlonuridae: *a*, *b*, *c*, maxilla and maxillary palps; *d*, *e*, *f*, labium and labial palps; *g*, *h*, *i*, *j*, markings on abdominal tergites. *a*, *d*, *g*, *Siphlonurus alternatus*; *b*, *e*, *h*, *S. armatus*; *c*, *f*, *i*, *S. lacustris*; *j*, *Ameletus inopinatus*. (Scale lines 0·5 mm above, 5 mm below).

## Family BAETIDAE

1 Six of the seven pairs of plate-like gills are double with usually one plate larger than the other (figs 9*a*, *b*, *c*, see also fig. 5*b*)— **2**

— All six or seven pairs of plate-like gills are single (figs 9*d*, *e*, 14*g*, *h*, *j*, see also figs 5*a*, *c*, *d*)— **4**

2 The six double gills have one plate much larger than the other, and both plates lack pointed tips (fig. 9*c*); no more than five dark rings on each tail between the tip of the abdomen and the median dark band on the tail (fig. 10*b*); body is sandy-coloured with strongly-contrasting light and dark areas on the abdomen (fig. 10*b*); tails held close together in live larva (fig. 10*b*)—

**Centroptilum pennulatum** Eaton

Larvae found chiefly in slow-flowing sections of streams and rivers, especially amongst vegetation and on sandy bottoms.

— The six double gills either have two plates of similar size but without pointed tips (fig. 9*a*), or have one plate much larger than the other and a pointed tip on the larger plate (fig. 9*b*); more than five dark rings on each tail between the tip of the abdomen and the median dark band (fig. 11*b*, *c*); body is sandy-coloured without strongly-contrasting light and dark areas on the abdomen; tails held well apart in live larvae (fig. 11*c*) and their tips curve downwards when viewed from the side (fig. 11*b*)— **3**

Fig. 9. Baetidae: *a-e*, gills of *a*, *Cloeon dipterum*; *b*, *C. simile*; *c*, *Centroptilum pennulatum*; *d*, third gill of *C. luteolum*; *e*, third gill of *Procloeon bifidum*. (Scale line 1 mm).

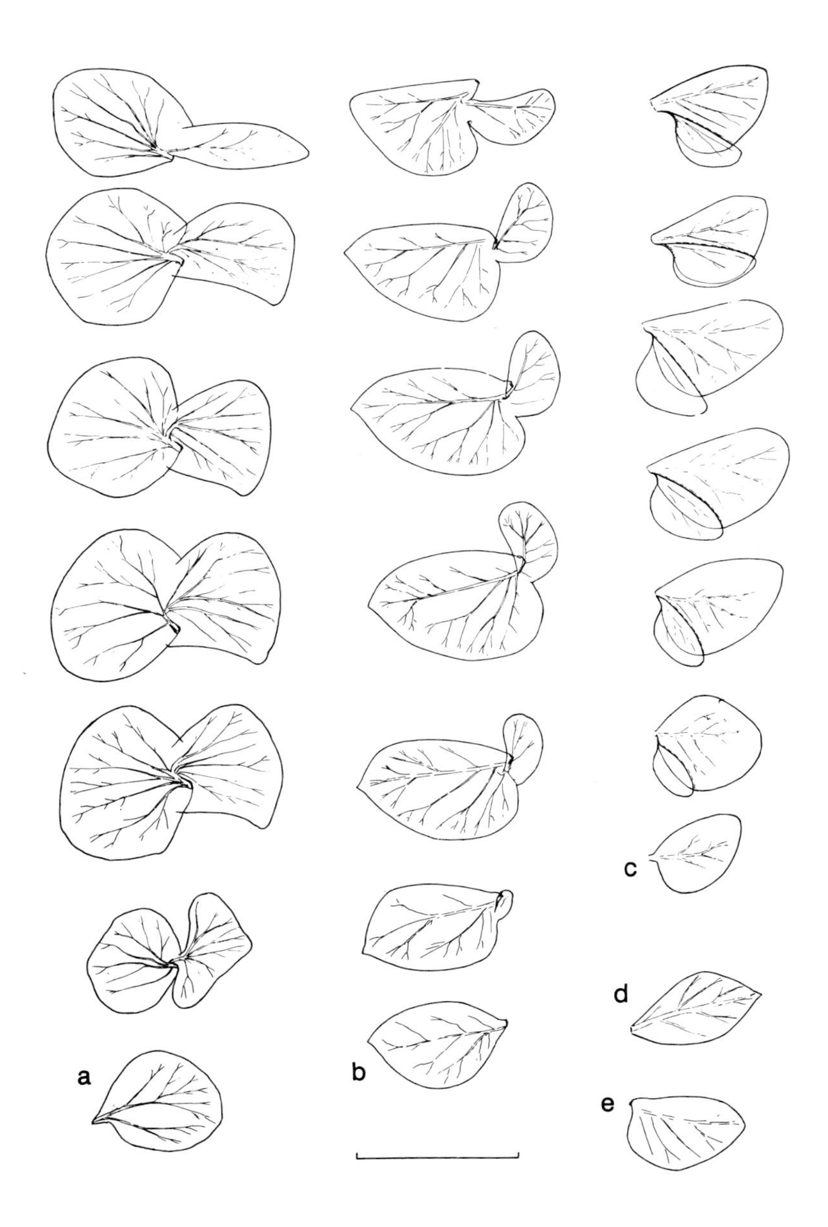
a
b
c
d
e

3 The six double gills have two plates of similar size and without pointed tips (fig. 9*a*, see also fig. 5*b*); maxillary palp has three segments (fig. 12*g*; if you are not sure which is the maxillary palp, check with fig. 1*b*); outer corner of last (terminal) segment of labial palp is elongated to form a point (fig. 12*a*)—

**Cloeon dipterum** (Linnaeus)

Larvae found chiefly in small productive ponds, shallow water in lakes and slow-flowing sections of streams and rivers.

— The six double gills have one plate much larger than the other and a pointed tip on the larger plate (fig. 9*b*); maxillary palp has two segments (fig. 12*h*); outer corner of last (terminal) segment of labial palp is not elongated (fig. 12*b*)— **Cloeon simile** Eaton

Larvae found chiefly in small ponds, slow-flowing sections of streams and rivers, and also amongst vegetation in the deeper water of ponds and lakes.

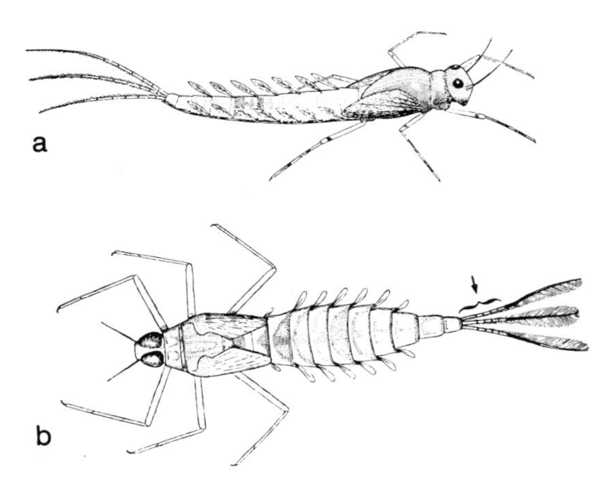


Fig. 10. Baetidae: *Centroptilum*. *a*, *C. luteolum*, 7 mm long, from life; *b*, *C. pennulatum*, 9 mm long, from life.

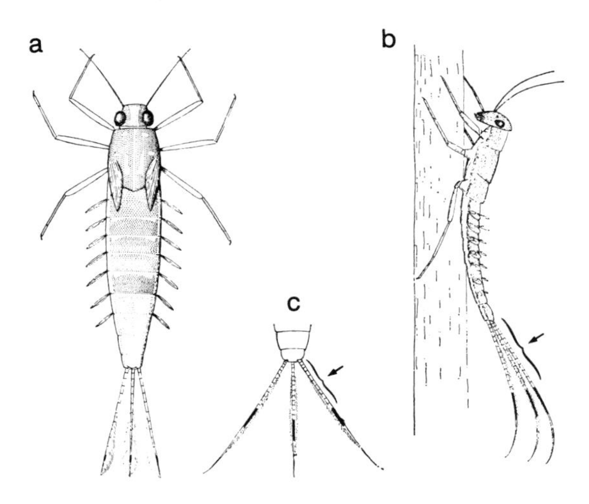


Fig. 11. Baetidae: *a*, *Procloeon bifidum*, 8 mm long, from life; *b*, *Cloeon dipterum*, 6 mm long (half grown), from life; *c*, hind end of *C. dipterum* in dorsal view, from life.

4(1) Each single gill shaped like a beech leaf with a pointed tip (fig. 9*d*, see also fig. 5*a*); tip of labial palp is distinctly concave (fig. 12*c*; if you are not sure which is the labial palp, check with fig. 1*b*); tails have dark rings but no wide dark band (figs 5*a*, 10*a*)—
**Centroptilum luteolum** (Müller)

Larvae found chiefly on stony shores of lakes and in slow-flowing sections of streams and rivers, especially amongst vegetation and on sandy bottoms.

— Each single gill without a distinct pointed tip (figs 9*e*, 14*g*, *h*, *j*); tip of labial palp not concave (figs 12*e*, *f*); tails have either dark rings, or a dark band, or neither a dark band nor rings (figs 11*a*, 16, 17, 19)—
**5**

5 All three tails are the same length and have dark rings (fig. 11*a*); second (penultimate) segment of labial palp does not have a protrusion on its inner distal corner (fig. 12*e*); each single gill is markedly asymmetrical (fig. 9*e*)— **Procloeon bifidum** (Bengtsson)

Larvae found chiefly in slow-flowing sections of streams and rivers.

— Middle tail is shorter than the outer ones (figs 5*c*, *d*, 16, 17, 19); tails never have dark rings but have a median dark band in some species (figs 16, 17, 19); second segment of labial palp has a distinct protrusion on its inner distal corner (figs 12*f*, 15*f*, *g*, *h*; the junction between the penultimate and terminal segments of the labial palp is usually indistinct so that the two segments appear as one and the end of the palp resembles a boxing-glove in most *Baetis* species); each single gill is almost symmetrical (figs 14*g*, *h*, *j*)— **Baetis 6**

(Note that the shorter middle tail, the absence of dark rings on the tails and the distinct labial palp are characters that separate the genus *Baetis* from all other genera in the family Baetidae.)

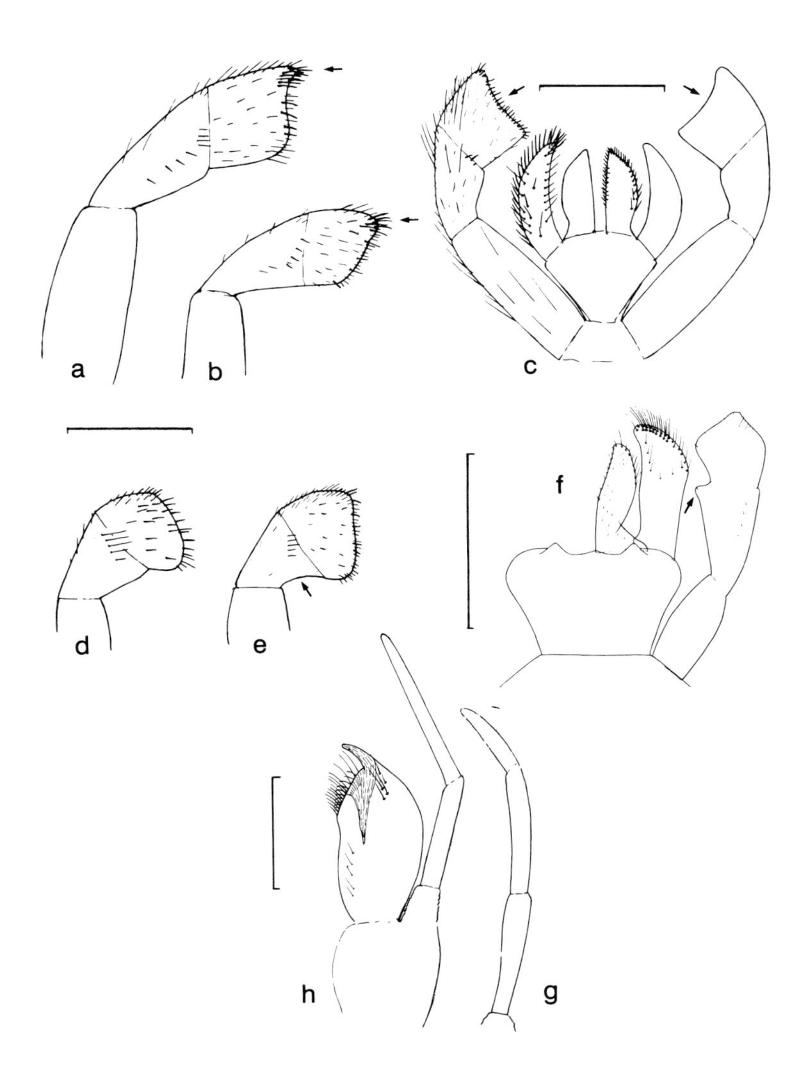


Fig. 12. Baetidae: *a-f*, labium and labial palps of *a*, *Cloeon dipterum*, *b*, *C. simile*; *c*, *Centroptilum luteolum*; *d*, *C. pennulatum*; *e*, *Procloeon bifidum*; *f*, *Baetis muticus*; *g-h* maxillary palp and maxilla of *g*, *Cloeon dipterum*; *h*, *C. simile*. (Scale lines 0·25 mm).

6 Bases of antennae are close together and the frons between them is reduced to a narrow triangle that points towards the anterior (figs 13*a*, *c*); head and thorax laterally compressed (narrow-bodied in appearance) so that the body tapers only slightly from the thorax to the tip of the abdomen (figs 16, 19*a*); first pair of gills on abdominal segment 1 (next to thorax) are either absent so that there are only six pairs of gills, or reduced so that they are much smaller than all other gills including the last (seventh) pair (figs 16*b*, 19*a*); first, outermost tooth on mandibles is small and set back from the other teeth, especially on the right mandible (figs 14*a*, *b*, *c*; if you are not sure which are the mandibles, check with fig. 1*b*)— 7

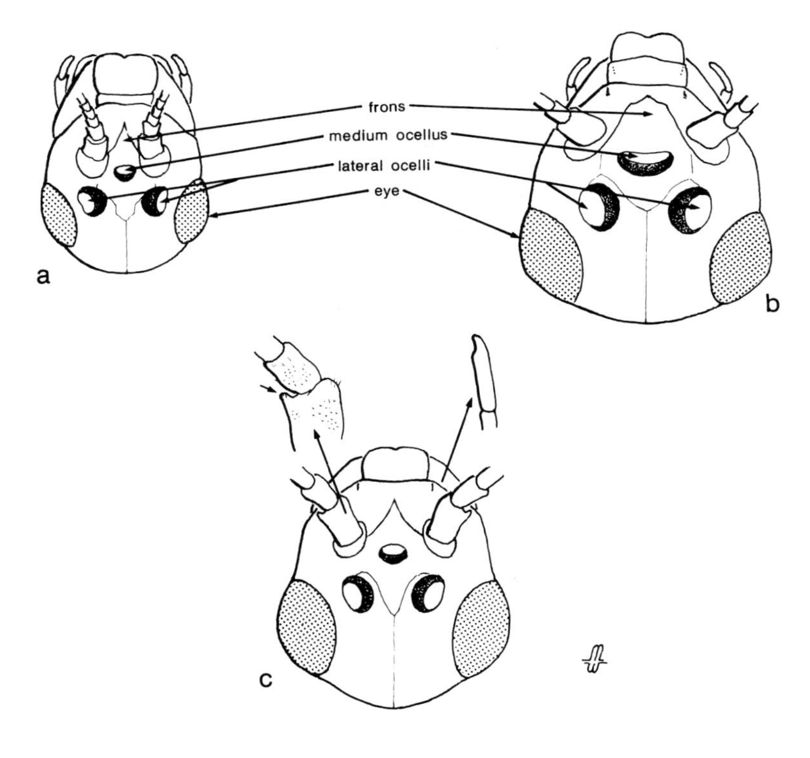


Fig. 13. Baetidae: *a-c*, dorsal surface of head capsule of *a*, *Baetis muticus*; *b*, *B. rhodani*; *c*, *B. atrebatinus* with enlarged views of right maxillary palp and basal segments of left antenna. (Original drawings by M. Mizzaro).

— Bases of antenna are wide apart and the frons between them is broad with an almost rectangular anterior edge (fig. 13*b*); head and thorax not laterally compressed (wide-bodied in appearance) so that the body tapers from the thorax to the tip of the abdomen and is generally fusiform, shaped like a spindle or cigar (figs 19*b*, *c*, *d*); first pair of gills are always present on abdominal segment 1 and are a similar size to the last (seventh) pair (fig. 19*b*); first, outermost tooth on mandibles is large and not set back (figs 14*d*, *e*)— **10**

(This couplet separates four narrow-bodied *Baetis* species, *atrebatinus*, *digitatus*, *muticus* and *niger*, from five wide-bodied species, *buceratus*, *fuscatus*, *rhodani*, *scambus* and *vernus*. The distance between the antennal bases and the shape of the frons are the easiest characters to use, but with practice the general body shape can be used to separate the two groups.)

Fig. 14. Baetidae: *Baetis*. *a-e*, canine area of the mandible of *a*, *B. niger*; *b*, *B. atrebatinus*; *c*, *B. muticus*; *d*, *B. scambus*; *e*, *B. rhodani*; *f*, right prostheca of *B. vernus*; *g-j*, third gill of *g*, *B. muticus*; *h*, *B. buceratus*; *j*, *B. vernus*. (Scale lines 0·1 mm).

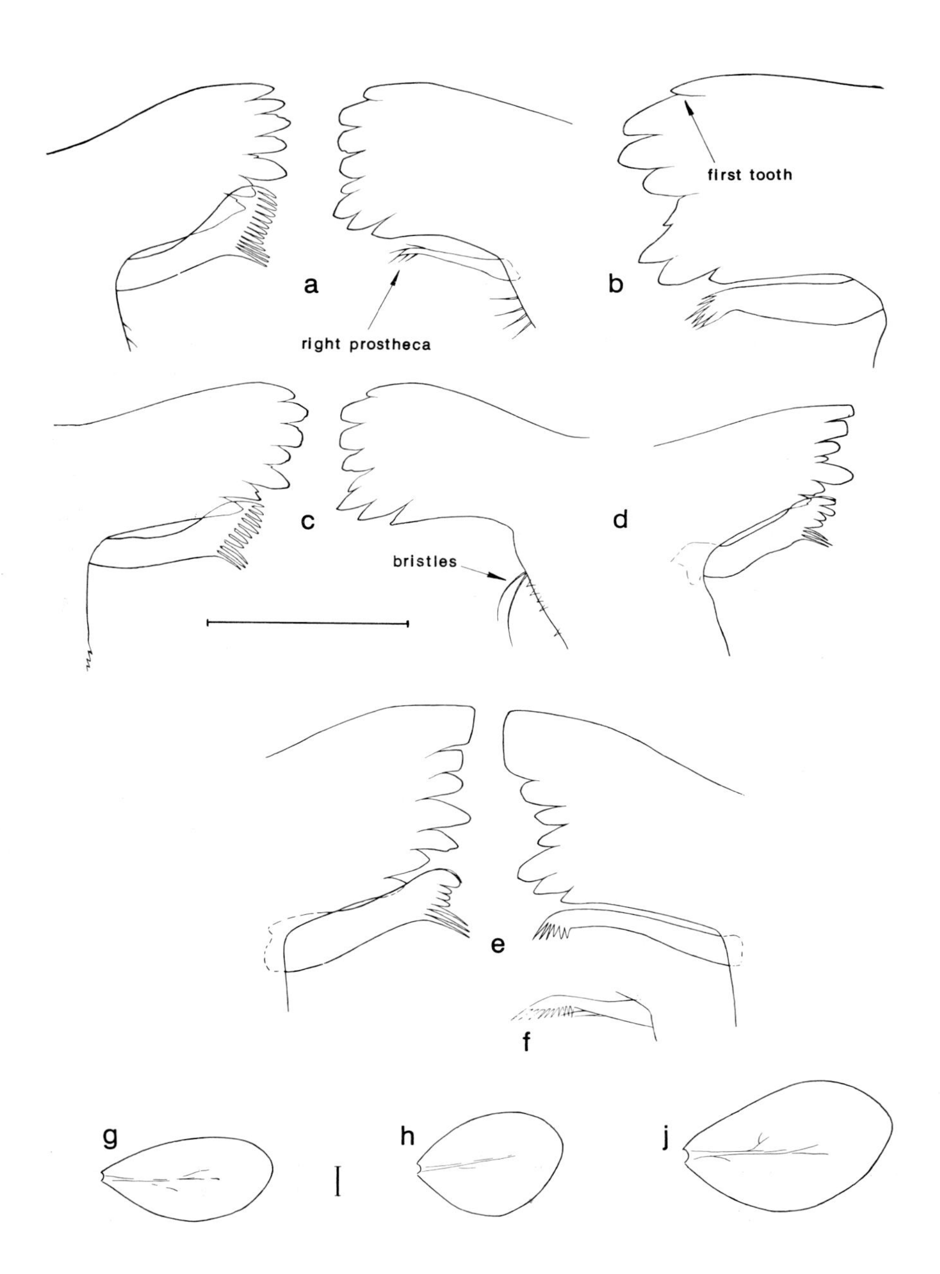

first tooth
a
b
right prostheca
c
d
bristles
e
f
g
h
j

7 Basal segment of antenna has a protrusion on its outer margin (fig. 13*c*); second segment of labial palp is very large so that the protrusion on its inner distal corner is as large as, or larger than, the terminal segment (fig. 15*f*); tip of maxillary palp is concave on its inner margin (figs 13*c*, 15*a*); labrum has a close-set row of 15-20 long bristles just behind the anterior margin (fig. 15*d*) (if you are not sure which are the appropriate mouthparts, check with fig. 1*b*)—
**Baetis atrebatinus** Eaton

(None of the above characters occur in any other British *Baetis* species.)

Larvae found chiefly in calcareous streams and rivers.

— Basal antennal segment has no distinct process; protrusion on labial palp is smaller than terminal segment (figs 12*f*, 15*g*, *h*); tip of maxillary palp is rounded; if there is a distinct line of long bristles behind the anterior margin of the labrum, they are well spaced and never exceed 10 in number (figs 15*b*, *c*, *e*)— **8**

Fig. 15. Baetidae: *Baetis*. *a*, maxillary palp of *B. atrebatinus*; *b-e*, labrum of *b*, *B. muticus*; *c*, *B. scambus*; *d*, *B. atrebatinus*; *e*, *B. rhodani*; *f-h*, labium of *f*, *B. atrebatinus*; *g*, *B. rhodani*; *h*, *B. vernus*. (Scale line 0·1 mm).

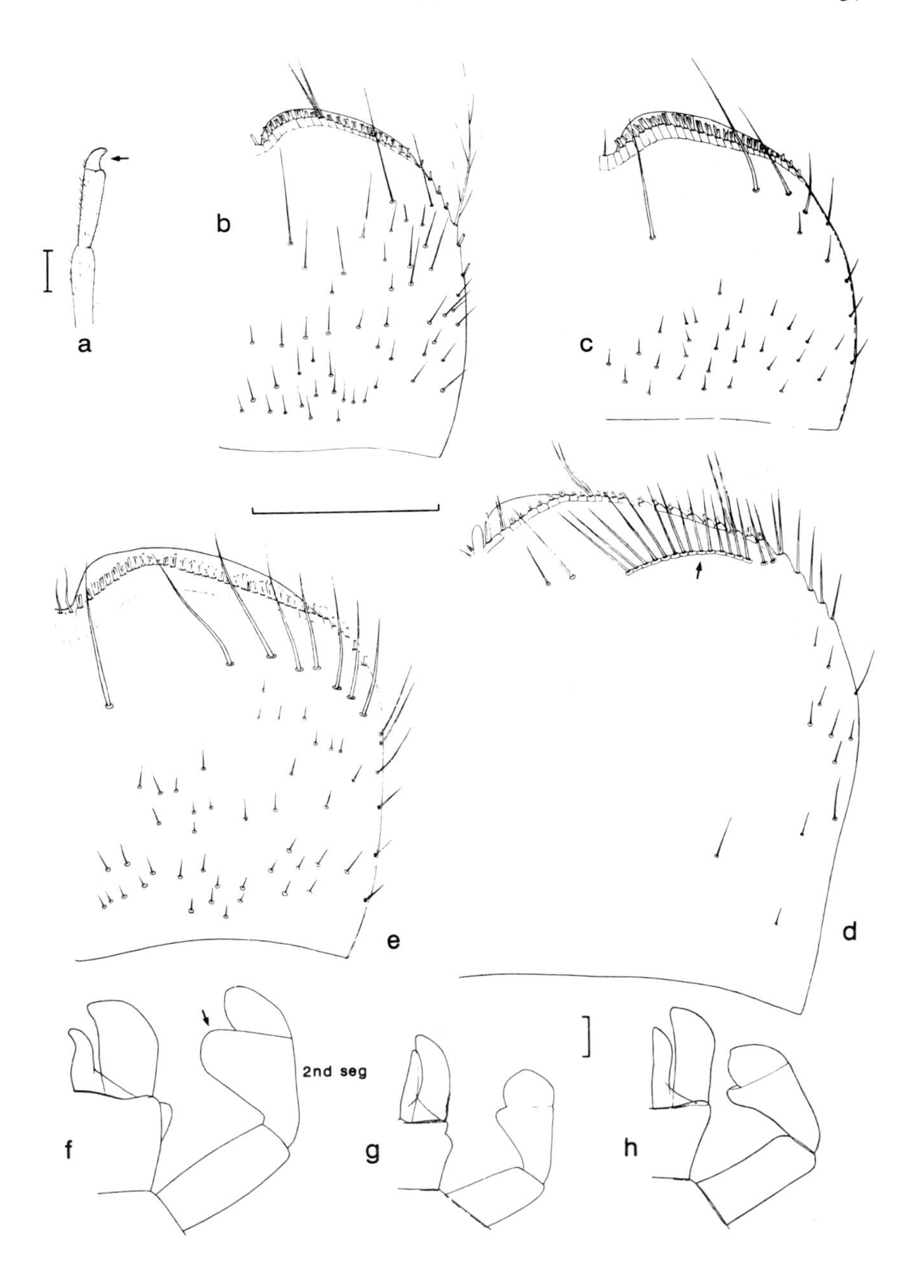
a
b
c
d
e
f
2nd seg
g
h

8 Seven pairs of gills are present on abdominal segments 1-7 (figs 16*b*, 19*a*); tails do not have a distinct black band near their middle; prostheca of right mandible is absent and replaced by two bristles (fig. 14*c*)— **Baetis muticus** (Linnaeus).

(The absence of a right prostheca is unique to this species and therefore separates it from all other *Baetis* species.)

Larvae found chiefly in stony streams and rivers, often deep in the substratum.

— Six pairs of gills are present on abdominal segments 2-7; tails have a distinct black band near their middle (fig. 16*e*); prostheca present on right mandible (fig. 14*a*)— **9**

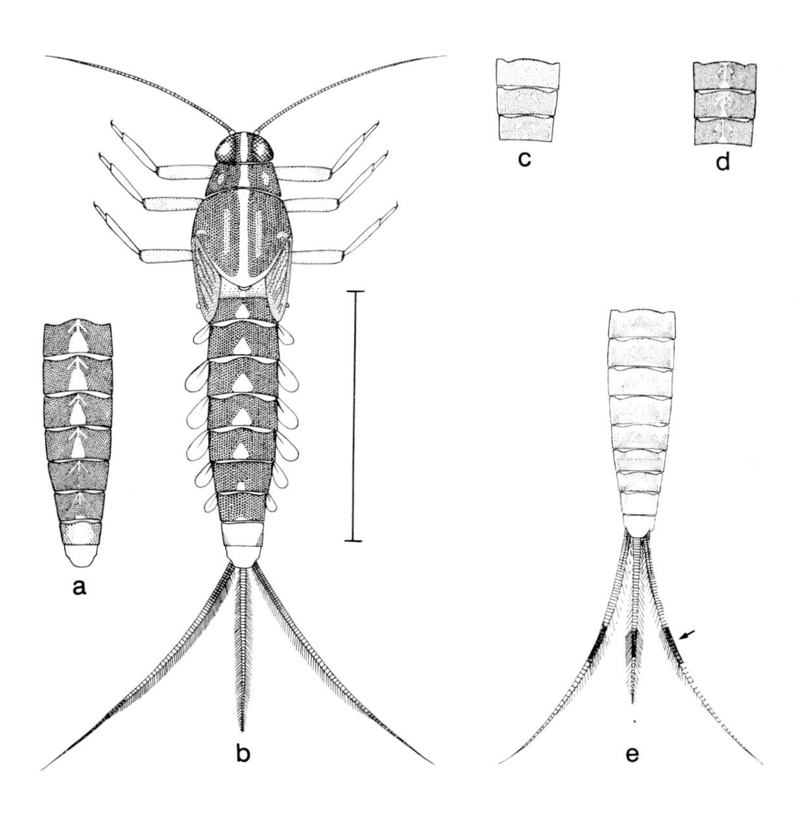


Fig. 16. Baetidae: *Baetis*. Patterns on the back of narrow-bodied species: *a*, *b*, *B. muticus*; *c*, *d*, *B. niger*; *e*, *B. digitatus*. (Scale line 5 mm).

9 Last pair of gills on abdominal segment 7 are oval and a similar shape to the other gills (fig. 17*a*); middle tail is only slightly shorter than the outer tails and is about three times the length of its median black band (fig. 17*c*)— **Baetis niger** (Linnaeus)

(Apart from *B. digitatus*, this is the only *Baetis* species with six pairs of gills.)

Larvae found chiefly amongst vegetation in streams and rivers.

— Last pair of gills on abdominal segment 7 are not oval, have a slightly concave hind edge (fig. 17*b*) and are therefore dissimilar to all the other gills, the latter being oval in shape; middle tail is only about two-thirds the length of the outer tails and is six to eight times the length of its black band (fig. 17*d*)— **Baetis digitatus** Bengtsson

(The shape of the last gill is unique to this species and therefore separates it from all other *Baetis* species.)

Larvae found chiefly amongst vegetation in streams and rivers.

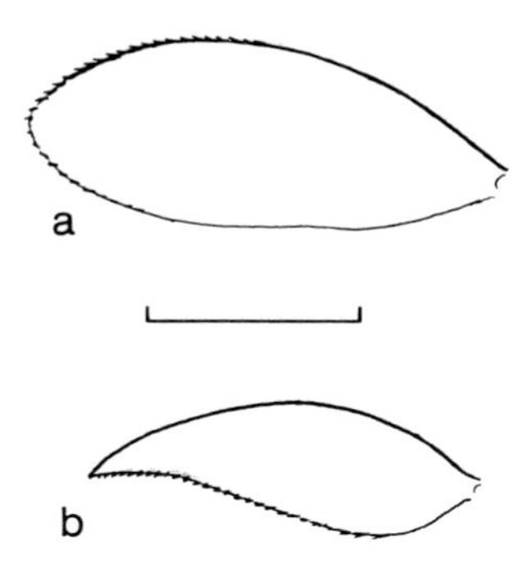


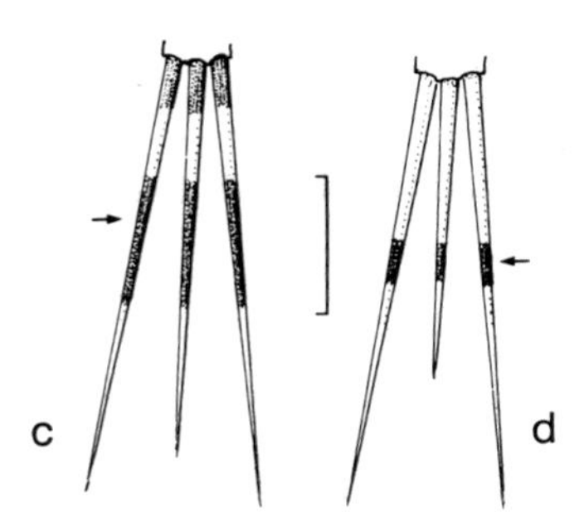


Fig. 17. Baetidae: *Baetis*. Right sixth gill (from abdominal segment 7) of *a*, *B. niger*; *B. digitatus*. (Scale line 0·1 mm). Tails of *c*, *B. niger*; *d*, *B. digitatus*. (Scale line 1 mm; original drawings by M. Mizzaro).

10(6) Long pointed spines occur intermittently amongst the hairs on the edge of each gill, ranging from about six spines on the smallest gill to about twenty spines on the largest gill (fig. 18*a*); stout, blunt spines occur on the abdominal tergites, both on the surface (among the scales) and along the posterior edge; similar spines occur on the basal segments of the antennae (fig. 18*b*)— **Baetis rhodani** (Pictet)

(None of the above characters occur in any other British *Baetis* species. The quickest method to identify *B. rhodani* is to remove one of the larger gills, mount it in water between a slide and coverslip, and examine the gill-edge for spines, using a magnification of 500-700x. Of the five wide-bodied *Baetis* species, *B. rhodani* can also be separated from *B. fuscatus* and *B. scambus* by the absence of a median black band across its tails (fig. 19*c*).)

Larvae found in streams and rivers; this is the commonest species in the genus (see also fig. 5*c*).

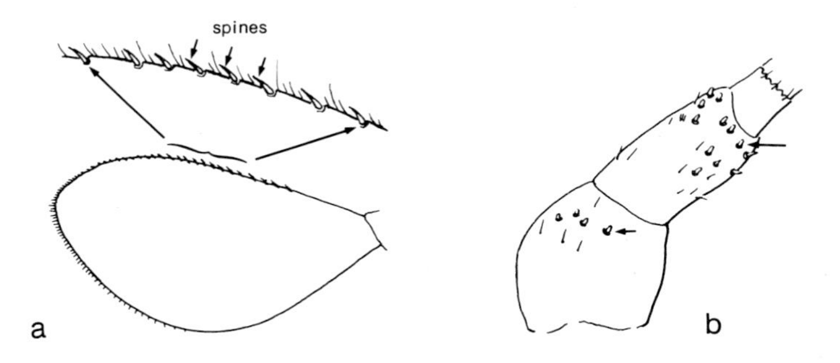


Fig. 18. Baetidae: *Baetis rhodani*. *a*, third gill with enlargement of margin to show spines between hairs; *b*, basal segments of right antenna, showing stout blunt spines. (Original drawings by M. Mizzaro).

— No spines occur on the edges of gills, abdominal tergites or basal segments of antennae— **11**

11 Tails have a median black band (fig. 19*b*); light oval marks are present on the abdominal tergites and are usually larger on tergite 5 which is therefore paler than all the other tergites and often gives the larva a characteristic pied appearance (fig. 19*b*)— **12**

— Tails have no distinct black band (i.e. they are similar to those of *B. rhodani* in fig. 19*c*); tergite 5 is not paler than other tergites (fig. 19*d*)— **13**

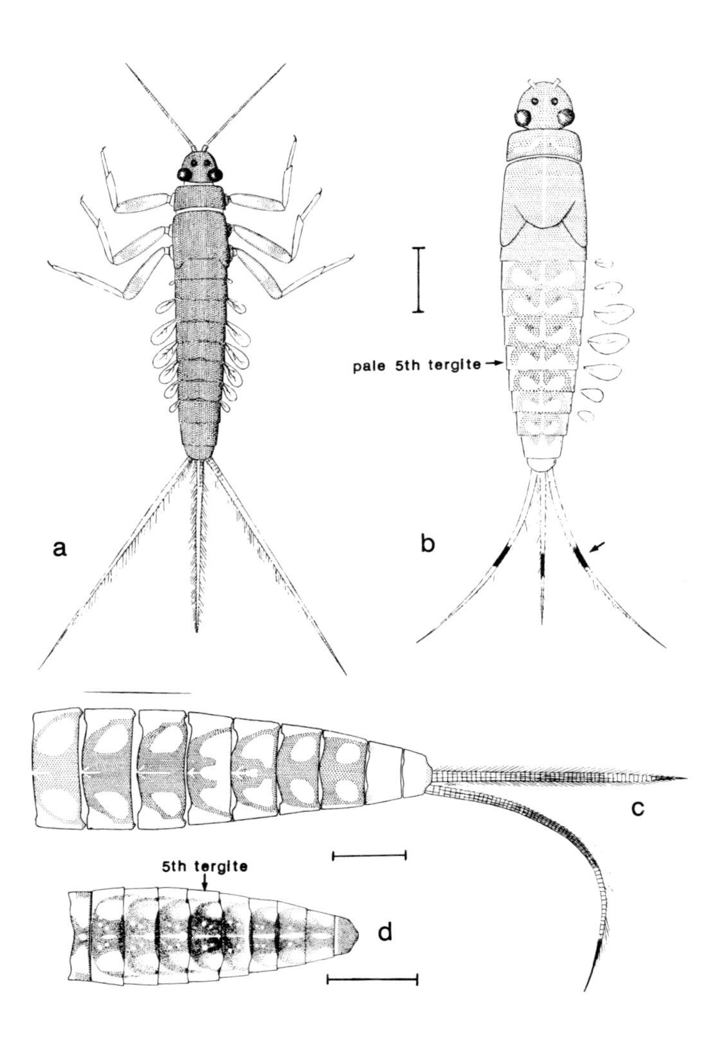


Fig. 19. Baetidae: *Baetis*. Narrow-bodied species: *a*, *B. muticus*. Wide-bodied species: *b*, *B. scambus*; *c*, *B. rhodani*; *d*, *B. buceratus*. (Scale lines 1 mm).

12 Irregularly-shaped marks on the dark background of the head capsule between the eyes are yellow-white and therefore conspicuous (these marks are the points of insertion of muscles) (fig. 20*a*); protrusion on the inner distal corner (fig. 20*c*) of the second segment of the labial palp projects slightly further than the slightly convex, inner surface of the terminal segment— **Baetis scambus** Eaton

Larvae found chiefly amongst vegetation and on sand and gravel in streams and rivers.

— Irregularly-shaped marks on the dark-brown background of the head capsule between the eyes are light-brown and therefore inconspicuous (fig. 20*b*); protrusion on the inner distal corner (fig. 20*d*) of the second segment of the labial palp projects only as far as the strongly convex, inner surface of the terminal segment— **Baetis fuscatus** (Linnaeus)

Larvae found chiefly amongst vegetation and on sand and gravel in rivers, possibly with a preference for calcareous waters.

(These two species are not easy to separate but unfortunately, no other reliable characters have been found.)

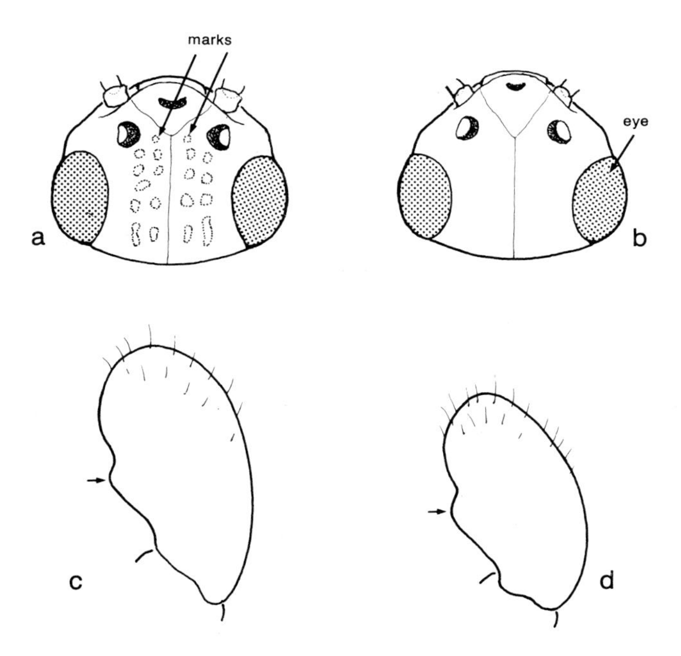


Fig. 20. Baetidae: *Baetis*. *a-b*, dorsal surface of head capsule of *a*, *B. scambus*; *b*, *B. fuscatus*; *c-d*, labial palp of *c*, *B. scambus*; *d*, *B. fuscatus*. (Original drawings by M. Mizzaro).

13(11) Light dots occur on most of the abdominal tergites (usually 4, sometimes 2, dots on each tergite, fig. 19*d*); first, outermost tooth on left mandible is about the same width as the second tooth (fig. 21*a*; if you are not sure which is the left mandible, check with fig. 1*b*); no auxiliary spines occur in the molar region of the left mandible (fig. 21*a*); comb-like end of prostheca of the right mandible is short (similar to that of *B. rhodani* in fig. 14*e*)— **Baetis buceratus** Eaton

Larvae found chiefly in rivers.

— No light dots occur on the abdominal tergites; first outermost tooth on left mandible is about twice the width of the second tooth (fig. 21*b*); small auxiliary spines (usually 2, sometimes 1 or 3) occur in the molar region of the left mandible (fig. 21*b*); comb-like end of prostheca of the right mandible is long (fig. 14*f*)— **Baetis vernus** Curtis

Larvae found chiefly in slow-flowing sections of rivers and in the upper reaches of small stony streams rising at high altitudes.

(These two species are not easy to separate but unfortunately, some previous characters given in Macan (1979) have been found to be unreliable (see comparisons in Armitage, Furse & Wright 1985). Note that the auxiliary spines on the left mandible of *B. vernus* also occur in *B. rhodani* but the right prostheca is markedly different in the two species (cf. figs 14*e* and *f*).)

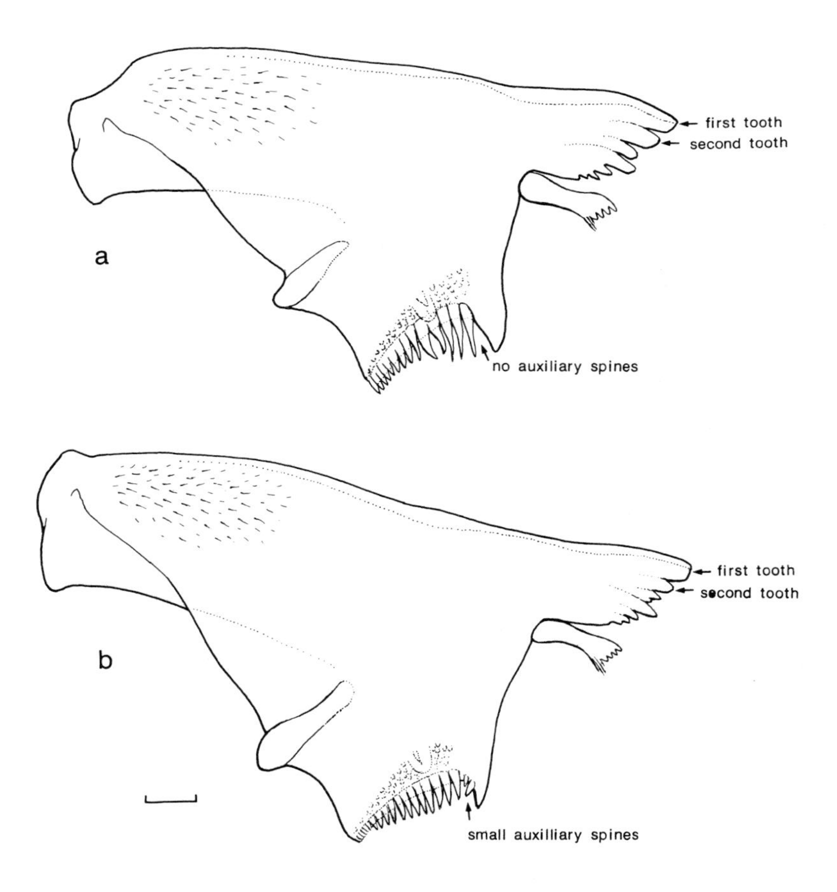


Fig. 21. Baetidae: *Baetis*. Dorsal view of left mandible of *a*, *B. buceratus*; *b*, *B. vernus*. (Scale line 0·1 mm; original drawings by M. Mizzaro).

## Family HEPTAGENIIDAE

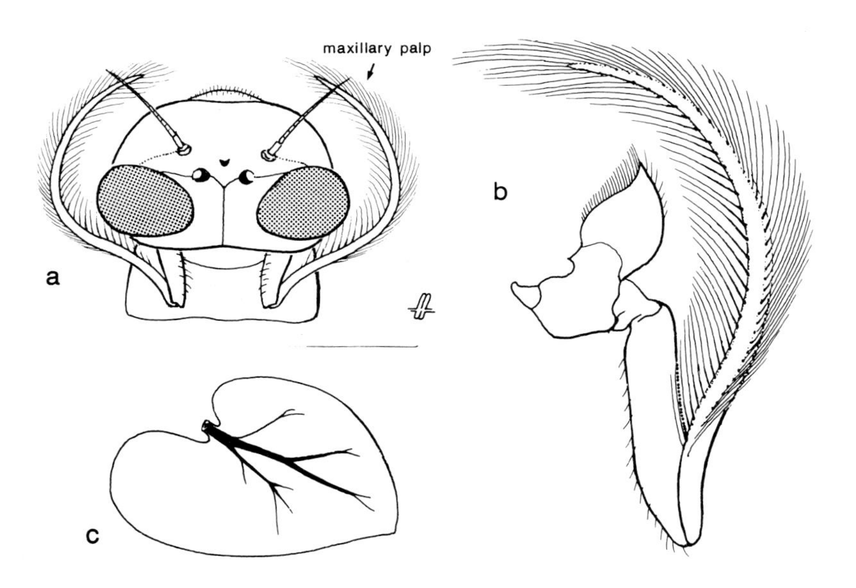


Fig. 22. Heptageniidae: *Arthroplea congener*. *a*, dorsal view of head; *b*, ventral view of left maxillary palp; *c*, sixth gill. (Original drawings by M. Mizzaro).

1 Long, brush-like maxillary palps extend well beyond edges of the head and are conspicuous in both dorsal and ventral view (fig. 22*a*, *b*); each gill is a flat plate without a separate tuft of filaments (fig. 22c)— **Arthroplea congener** Bengtsson

Larvae found chiefly in slow-flowing water. This species may no longer occur in the British Isles; the only record is a single adult male collected by R. South at Stanmore, Middlesex on 4 June 1920 (see Blair 1929).

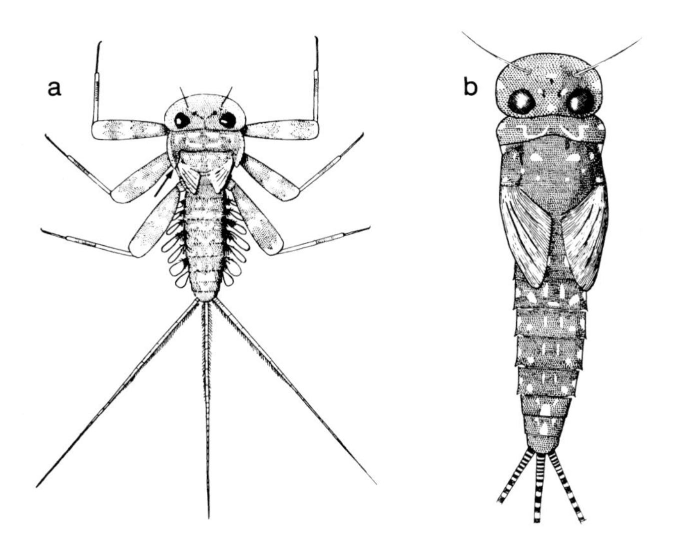


Fig. 23. Heptageniidae: *a*, *Ecdyonurus venosus* (length 11 mm); *b*, *Heptagenia sulphurea* (length 12 mm).

— Maxillary palps are not as in fig. 22 and are shorter than the head; tufts of filaments are present on all, or some of the plate-like gills (figs 3*d*, 4*a*, 23*a*)— **2**

2 Pronotum (first anterior segment of thorax) has a backward projection on either side (figs 4*a*, 23*a*)— **3**

— Pronotum without backward projections (figs 3*d*, 23*b*)— **6**

3 Each of the seven pairs of gills has a flat plate and a tuft of filaments— **Ecdyonurus insignis** (Eaton)

Larvae found chiefly in stony rivers.

— Last, most posterior gill does not have a tuft of filaments (e.g. fig. 23*a*)— **4**

4 Lateral margins of the pronotum are strongly curved (proportion $\alpha/\beta>4.5$) (fig. 24*a*); glossa of the labium is short and round (fig. 24*d*); if you are not sure which is the labium, check with figs 1*b*, 24*g*)—
**Ecdyonurus dispar** (Curtis)

Larvae found chiefly in stony rivers and on the stony shores of lakes.

— Lateral margins of the pronotum are only slightly curved (proportion $\alpha/\beta<4.0$ (figs 24*b*, *c*); glossa is elongated (figs 24*e*, *f*)— **5**

Fig. 24. Heptageniidae: *Ecdyonurus*. *a-c*, right half of pronotum of *a*, *E. dispar*; *b*, *E. torrentis*; *c*, *E. venosus*; *d-f*, glossa of *d*, *E. dispar; e*, *E. torrentis*; *f*, *E. venosus*; *g*, ventral view of half of labium, showing position of glossa (see also fig. 1*b*). (Scale lines 0·5 mm; original drawings by M. Mizzaro).

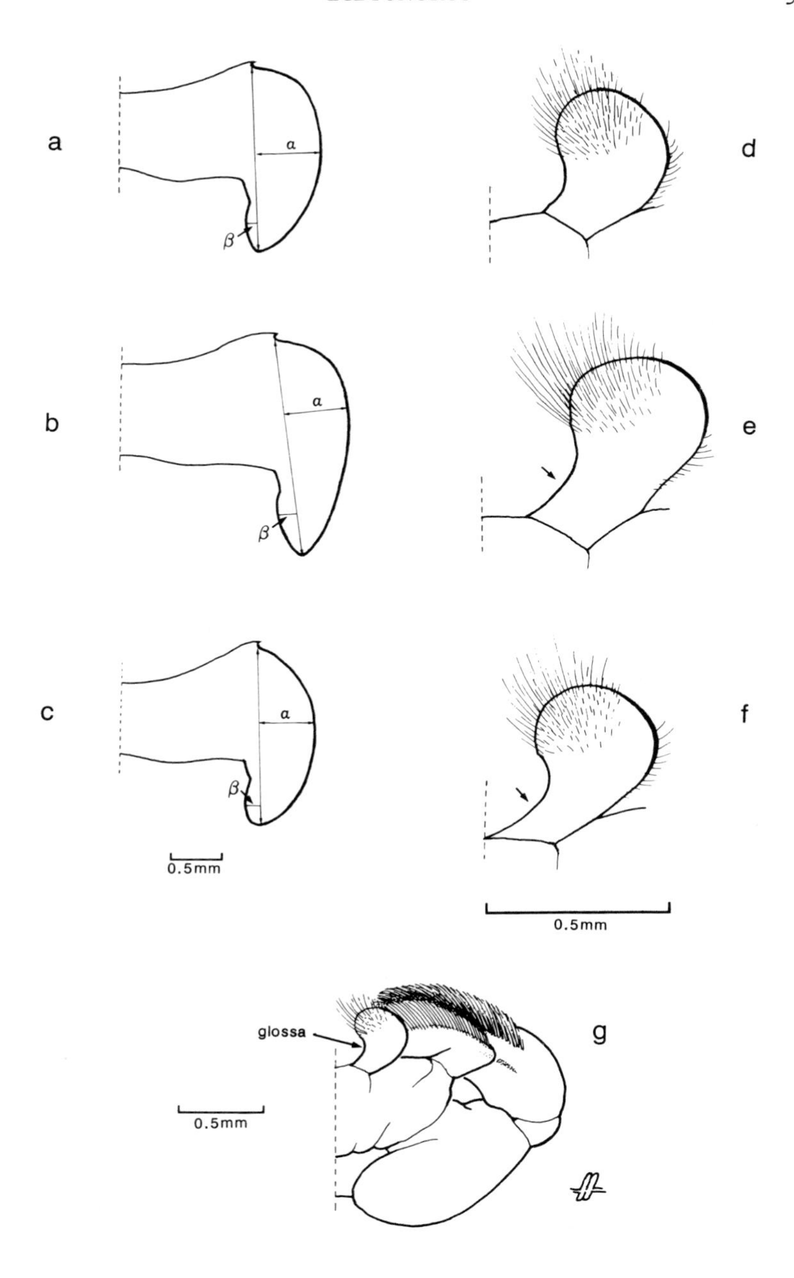
a
α
β
d
b
α
β
e
c
α
β
f
0.5mm
0.5mm
glossa
g
0.5mm

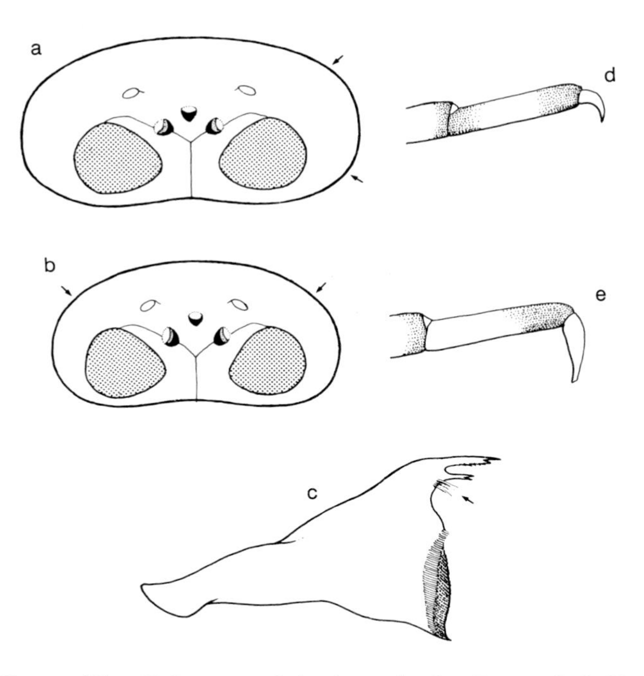


Fig. 25. Heptageniidae: *Ecdyonurus*. *a-b*, head capsule of *a*, *E. torrentis*; *b*, *E. venosus*; *c*, ventral view of right mandible, showing location of prosthecal setae; *d-e*, tarsus of *d*, *E. torrentis*; *e*, *E. venosus*. (Original drawings by M. Mizzaro).

5 Head capsule is rectangular (fig. 25*a*); less than 10 setae in prostheca of mandible (fig. 25*c*; if you are not sure which is the mandible, check with fig. 1*b*); each tarsus has dark bands near its base and near the claw (fig. 25*d*)— **Ecdyonurus torrentis** Kimmins

Larvae found in stony streams and rivers.

— Head capsule is rounded (fig. 25*b*); more than 10 setae in prostheca; each tarsus has a dark band near the claw (fig. 25*e*)— **Ecdyonurus venosus** (Fabricius)

Larvae found in stony streams and rivers.

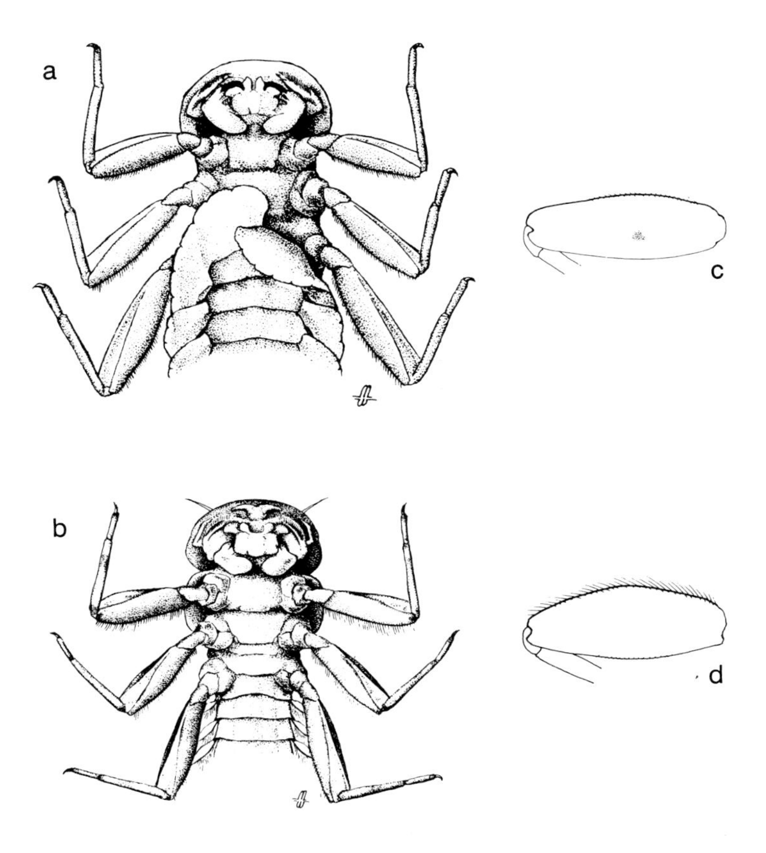


Fig. 26. Heptageniidae: *a-b*, position of gills of *a*, *Rhithrogena*; *b*, *Heptagenia*; *c-d*, dorsal view of femur of *c*, *Rhithrogena*; *d*, *Heptagenia*. (Original drawings by M. Mizzaro).

6(2) First gill is very large and meets its fellow beneath the body (fig. 26*a*); each femur has a dark dot in the centre (fig. 26*c*)— **7**

— First gill is small and like the others in shape (fig. 26*b*); femora without a dark dot (fig. 26*d*)— **8**

7 Gills 2-7 are rectangular in shape (fig. 27*a*); labrum is broad, the proportion of the length to the width is approximately 1 : 2 (fig. 27*c*); the inner incisivus of the mandible is not broadened on the top (27*e*); the hypopharynx is smaller on the top (27*g*)—

**Rhithrogena germanica** Eaton

Large specimens; larvae recorded only from a small number of large rivers.

— Gills 2-7 are oval in shape (fig. 27*b*); labrum is small, the proportion of the length to the width is approximately 1 : 3 (fig. 27*d*); the inner incisivus of the mandible is broadened on its top (fig. 27*f*); the hypopharynx is not smaller on the top (fig. 27*h*)—

**Rhithrogena semicolorata** (Curtis)

Larvae found in stony streams and rivers.

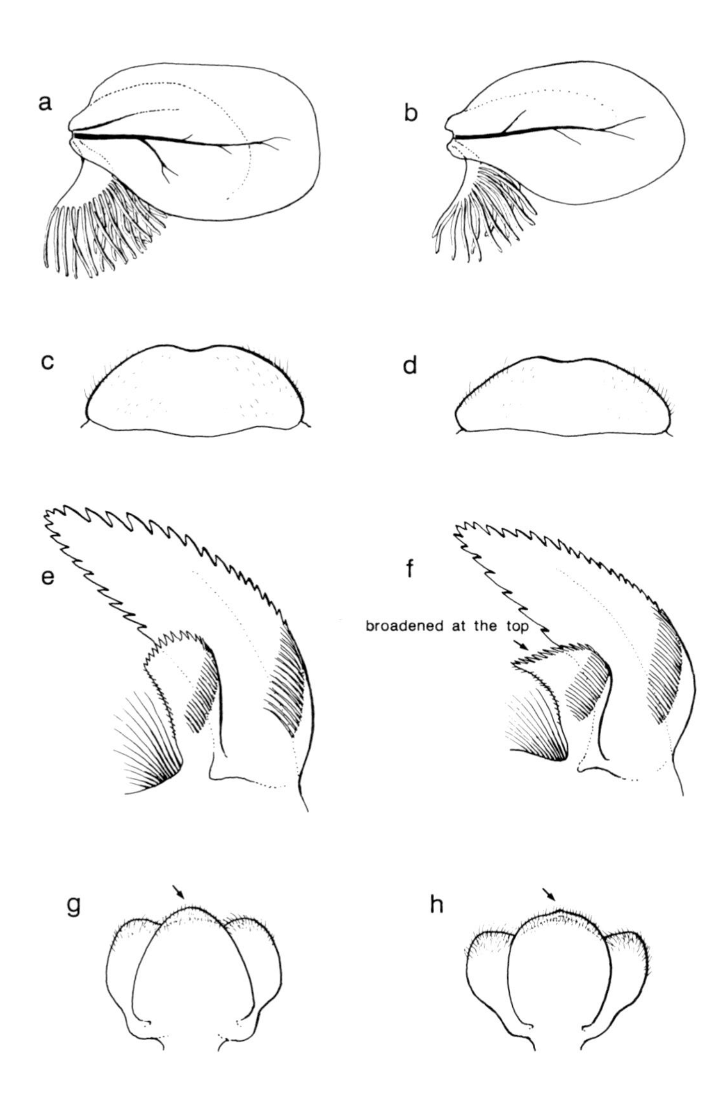


Fig. 27. Heptageniidae: *Rhithrogena*. *a*, *b*, dorsal view of gills; *c*, *d*, labrum; *e*, *f*, dorsal view of inner incisivius of right mandible; *g*, *h*, ventral view of hypopharynx. *a*, *c*, *e*, *g*, *R. germanica*; *b*, *d*, *f*, *h*, *R. semicolorata*. (Original drawings by M. Mizzaro).

8(6) Filamentous part of all gills is as large as the flat plate—
**Heptagenia longicauda** (Stephens)

Larvae found chiefly in large rivers (this species may no longer occur in the British Isles)

— Filamentous part of some gills is smaller than the flat plate (fig. 28*a-c*)— **9**

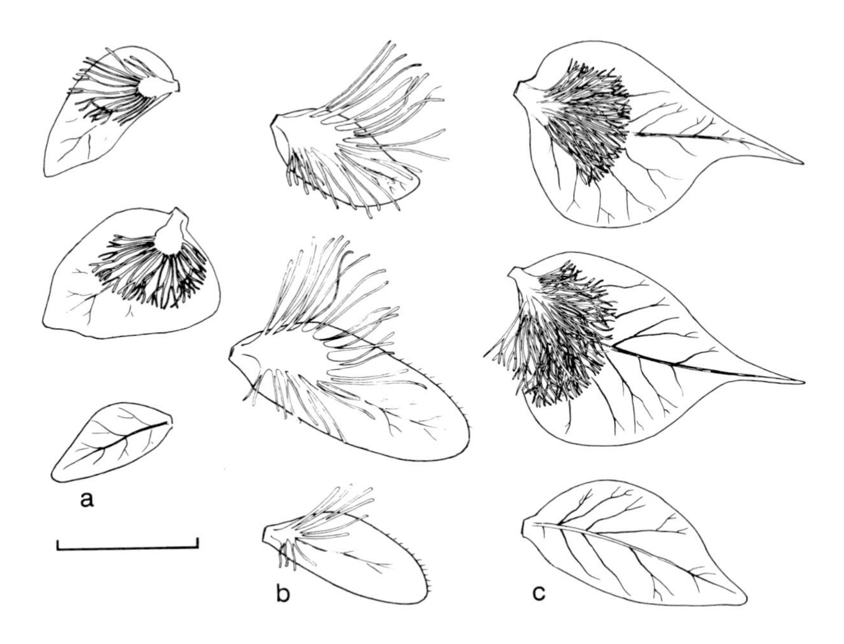


Fig. 28. Heptageniidae: *Heptagenia*. *a-c*, first (top), fourth and seventh gills of *a*, *H. lateralis*; *b*, *H. sulphurea*; *c*, *H. fuscogrisea*. (Scale line 1 mm).

9 Little or no pattern occurs on body and tails; a light cross-shaped area on the femur separates four dark areas which are often darker in the middle (fig. 29*a*); upper margin of femur is fringed with hairs, which, if folded back, would extend more than half-way across the femur (fig. 29*d*); gills narrow gradually to a rather blunt point (the seventh without a tuft of filaments) (fig. 28*a*)—
**Heptagenia lateralis** (Curtis)

Larvae found in stony streams, rivers and on the stony shores of lakes.

— Body has a conspicuous black-and-white pattern (fig. 23*b*); femur has transverse bars (fig. 29*b*, *c*); hairs along upper margin of femur are short (fig. 29*e*, *f*); gills are either rounded or sharply pointed (fig. 28*b*, *c*)— **10**

10 Gills are rather small and rounded at tip, the last gill (seventh) with a tuft of filaments (fig. 28*b*); femur has black transverse bands (fig. 29*b*) and its fore margin has a fringe of short hairs and spines (fig. 29*e*)— **Heptagenia sulphurea** (Müller)

Larvae are chiefly found in rivers draining calcareous areas and in the lower reaches of rivers. In Ireland they are abundant in limestone lakes, whereas *H. lateralis* occurs in non-calcareous lakes.

— Gills are large and produced into a point, the last gill without a tuft of filaments (fig. 28*c*); femur has two reddish-brown bands (fig. 29*c*) and its fore-margin has a few short hairs along the distal part (fig. 29*f*)— **Heptagenia fuscogrisea** (Retzius)

This species is rare in England but larvae are common in lakes in limestone areas of Ireland; on stony substrata but also, unlike other members of the family, in vegetation (Madsen 1968).

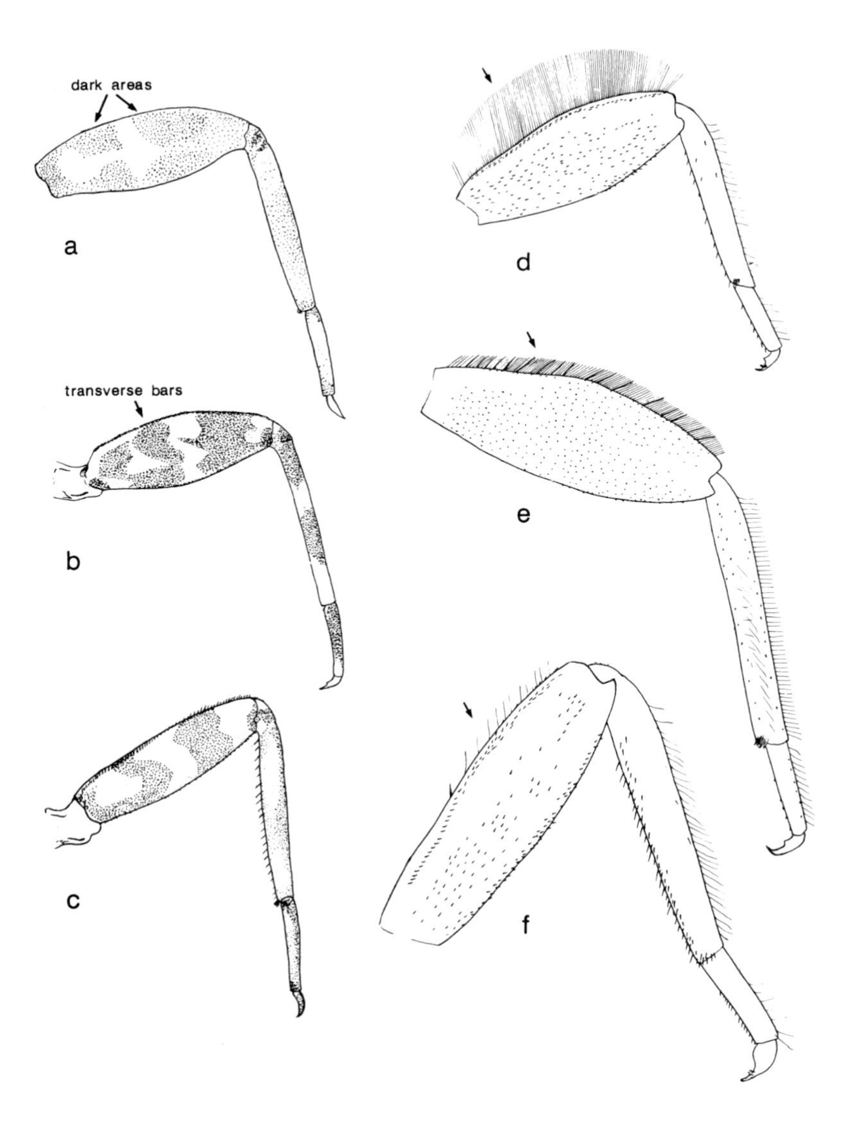


Fig. 29. Heptageniidae: *Heptagenia*. *a-c*, leg markings and *d-f*, details of middle legs of *a*, *d*, *H. lateralis*; *b*, *e*, *H. sulphurea*; *c*, *f*, *H. fuscogrisea*. (Scale lines 1 mm; spines 0·1 mm).

## Family LEPTOPHLEBIIDAE

1 All seven pairs of gills are similar in shape and each gill has several branches (figs 4*c*, 30*a*)— **Habrophlebia fusca** (Curtis)

Larvae found chiefly in slow-flowing streams with aquatic macrophytes or dead leaves, sometimes in rivers.

— Each gill has only two branches (figs 30*b*, *c*, *d*, *e*)— 2

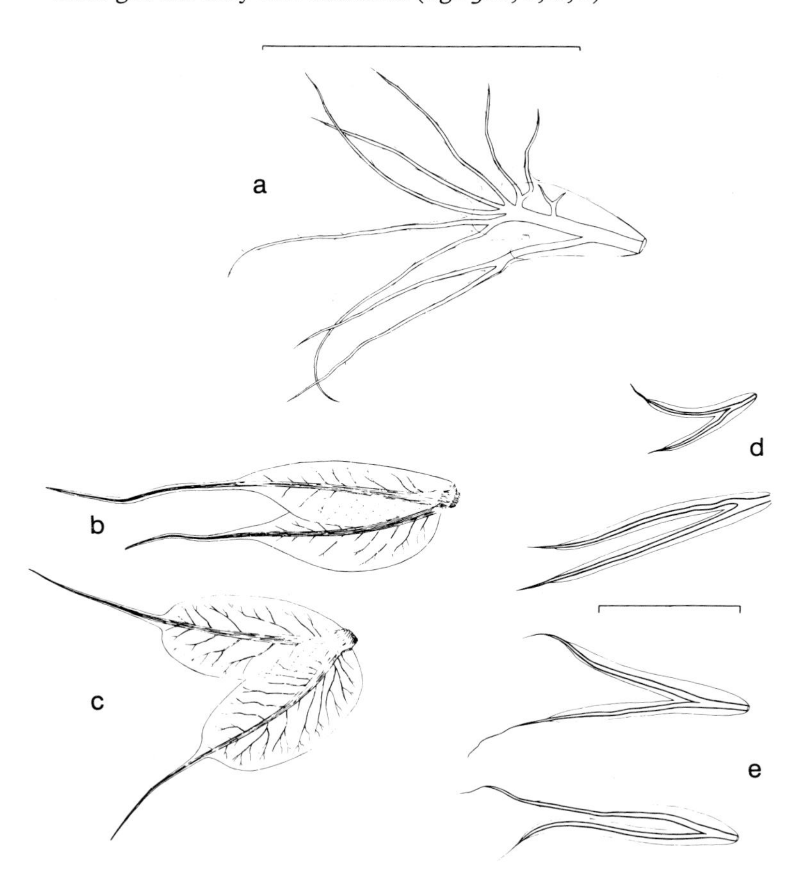


Fig. 30. Leptophlebiidae: *a-c*, fourth gills of *a*, *Habrophlebia fusca*; *b*, *Leptophlebia vespertina*; *c*, *L. marginata*; *d-e*, first and second gills of *d*, *Paraleptophlebia submarginata*; *e*, *P. werneri*. (Scale line 1 mm).

2 Two branches of first gill are strap-shaped; remaining six pairs of gills have two plates, each tapering to a single filament (figs 30*b*, *c*)— **Leptophlebia 3**

— Two branches of all seven pairs of gills are strap-shaped (figs 30*d*, *e*)— **Paraleptophlebia 4**

(In the early instars with a body length less than 3 mm, the gills of both genera are strap-shaped, but the mouthparts can be used to separate the genera. In *Leptophlebia*, the maxillary palp is short, only about half its length extending beyond the maxilla, and the tip of the palp carries only short hairs (fig. 31*a*). In *Paraleptophlebia*, the maxillary palp is long, about two-thirds of its length extending beyond the maxilla, and the tip of the palp carries long hairs (figs 31*b*, *c*). If you are not sure which is the maxilla, check with fig. 1*b*.)

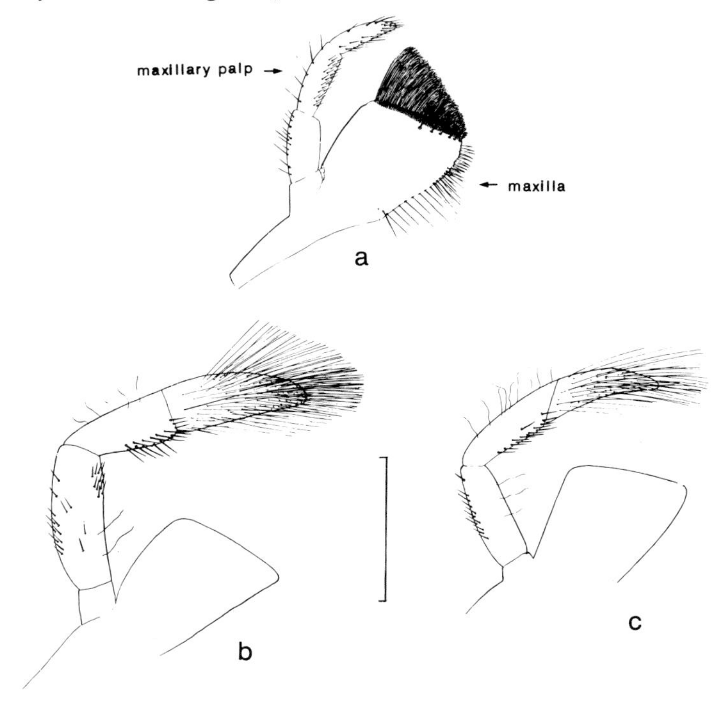


Fig. 31. Leptophlebiidae: maxillary palp and maxilla of *a*, *Leptophlebia vespertina*; *b*-*c*, maxillary palp and outline of maxilla of *b*, *Paraleptophlebia submarginata*; *c*, *P. cincta*. (Scale line 0·5 mm).

3 In mature larvae, the junction of each gill plate and its terminal filament is gradual (fig. 30*b*); in all larvae teeth cover nearly all the length of the claw (fig. 32*a*); some spines on lower edge of femur of fore leg have many sharp projections, some of which may be simply hairs (fig. 32*d*; these complex spines are obvious on a detached fore leg viewed at a magnification of about 100×)—
**Leptophlebia vespertina** (Linnaeus)

Larvae found chiefly in ponds, lakes and slow-flowing streams.

— In mature larvae, the junction of each gill plate and its terminal filament is abrupt (fig. 30*c*); in all larvae, teeth cover only two-thirds of the length of the claw (fig. 32*b*); spines on lower edge of femur of fore leg have a single point (fig. 32*e*; the spines appear simple at a magnification of about 100×, but under a higher magnification of about 400×, they are seen to be fringed with tiny hairs)—
**Leptophlebia marginata** (Linnaeus)

Larvae found chiefly in ponds, lakes and slow-flowing streams. This is the largest of the two *Leptophlebia* spp.; length of mature larvae from front of head to tip of abdomen is 10.5-11.5 mm for *L. marginata* and 7-10 mm for *L. vespertina*.

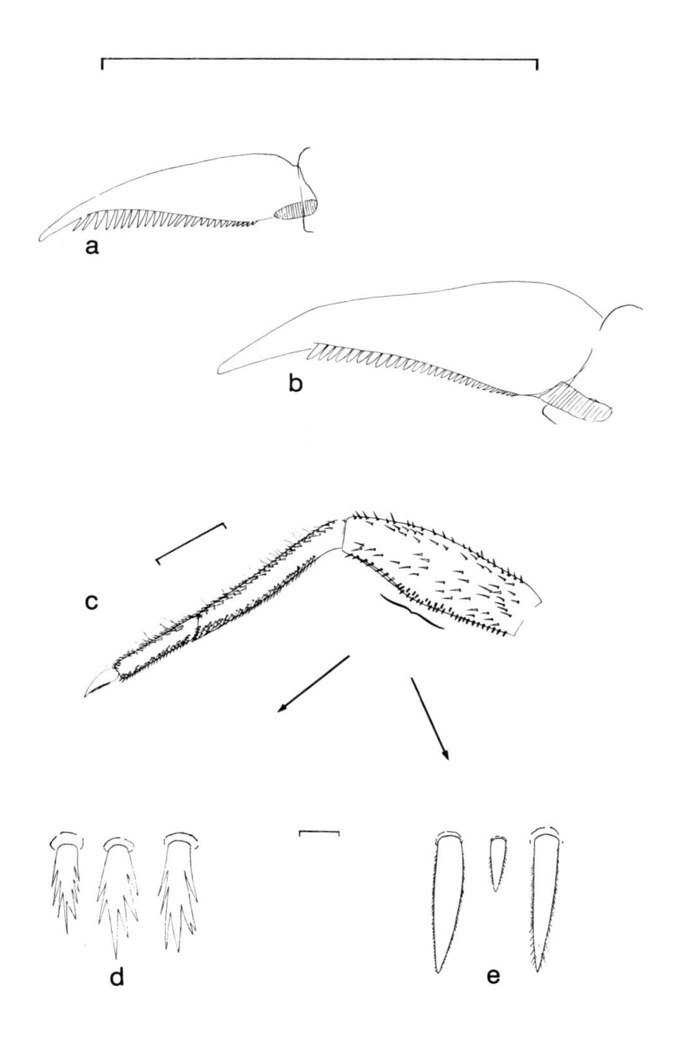


Fig. 32. Leptophlebiidae: *a-b*, hind claws of *a*, *Leptophlebia vespertina*; *b*, *L. marginata* (Scale line 0·5 mm); *c*, fore leg of *Leptophlebia* (Scale line 0·5 mm). *d-e*, spines from the lower edge of femur of fore leg of *d*, *L. vespertina*; *e*, *L. marginata* (Scale line 0·01 mm).

4(2) Gill-size decreases slightly and progressively from the fourth to seventh pair, and from the fourth to second pair, but then decreases markedly from the second to first pair (gills nearest thorax) so that both branches of the first gill are about half to two-thirds the length of those of the second gill (fig. 30*d*); spines on lower edge of femur of hind leg are columnar with blunt tips (fig. 33*a*)—
**Paraleptophlebia submarginata** (Stephens)

Larvae found chiefly in stony streams and rivers. (Note that the teeth cover just over half the length of the claw as in *P. cincta*, fig. 33*e*).

— Gill-size decreases slightly and progressively from the fourth to seventh pair, and from the fourth to first pair so that the first gill is only slightly smaller than the second (fig. 30*e*); spines on lower edge of femur of hind leg are tapering with either pointed tips (fig. 33*b*) or blunt tips (fig. 33*c*)— **5**

5 Teeth cover about three-quarters of the length of the claw (fig. 33*d*); spines on lower edge of femur of hind leg are tapering with pointed tips (fig. 33*b*)— **Paraleptophlebia werneri** Ulmer

Larvae found chiefly in calcareous streams with abundant vegetation, and also in streams that cease to flow in summer.

— Teeth cover just over half the length of the claw (fig. 33*e*); spines on lower edge of femur of hind leg are tapering with blunt tips (fig. 33*c*)— **Paraleptophlebia cincta** (Retzius)

Larvae found chiefly in streams and rivers.

(The quickest method to separate these species is to remove one of the hind legs, mount it in water between a slide and coverslip, and examine first the teeth on the claws, then the spines on the femur, using a magnification of about 100×.)

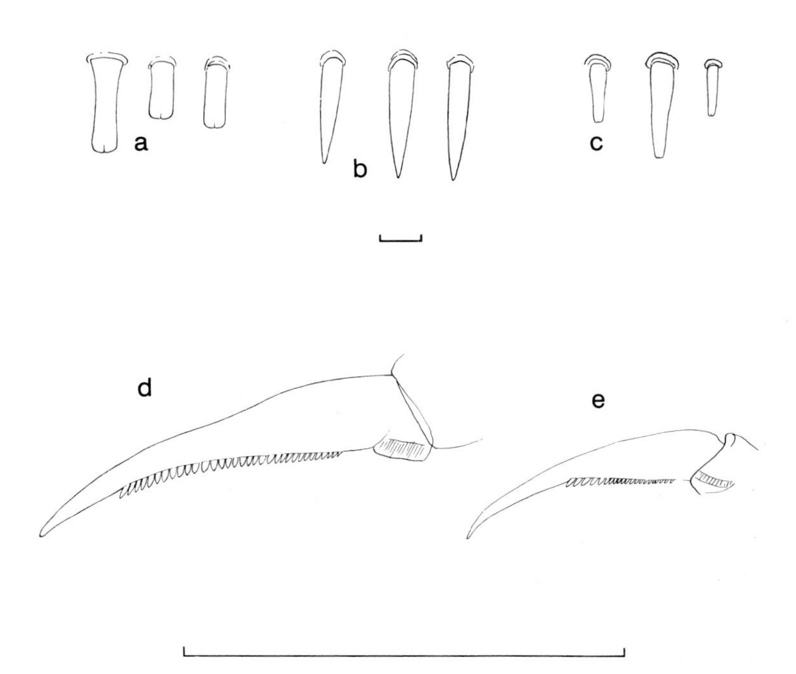


Fig. 33. Leptophlebiidae: *a-c*, spines from the lower edge of femur of hind leg of *a*, *Paraleptophlebia submarginata*; *b*, *P. werneri*; *c*, *P. cincta* (Scale line 0·01 mm). *d-e*, hind claws of *d*, *P. werneri*; *e*, *P. cincta* (Scale line 0·5 mm).

## Family POTAMANTHIDAE

Only one species occurs in the British Isles and is easily identified from the characters given in the key to families (figs 2, 3*c*)—
**Potamanthus luteus** (Linnaeus)

Larvae found chiefly in large rivers, often in side pools with a bottom of stones and sand.

## Family EPHEMERIDAE

1 Two triangular marks on each abdominal tergite, except sometimes the first and last, and a pair of longitudinal stripes on tergites 7-9 (fig. 34*a*); tibia of fore leg (also middle leg) rather narrow with its inner margin formed by two straight lines joined by a short curve (fig. 34*d*) (femur narrow)— **Ephemera vulgata** Linnaeus

Larvae found chiefly in rivers with a muddy bottom.

— Abdominal markings are not as above (figs 34*b*, *c*); tibia of fore leg (also middle leg) rather broad with its inner margin distinctly curved (figs 34*e*, *f*)— **2**

2 Two triangular marks on abdominal tergites 7-9 with sometimes a paler line inside each triangle (fig. 34*b*); femur of fore leg relatively narrow (fig. 34*e*)— **Ephemera danica** Müller

Larvae found chiefly in lakes and fast-flowing streams and rivers with a sandy or gravelly bottom.

— Six longitudinal stripes on abdominal tergites 7-9 (fig. 34*c*); femur of fore leg relatively broad (fig. 34*f*)— **Ephemera lineata** Eaton

Larvae found chiefly in large rivers, e.g. Rivers Wye and Thames.

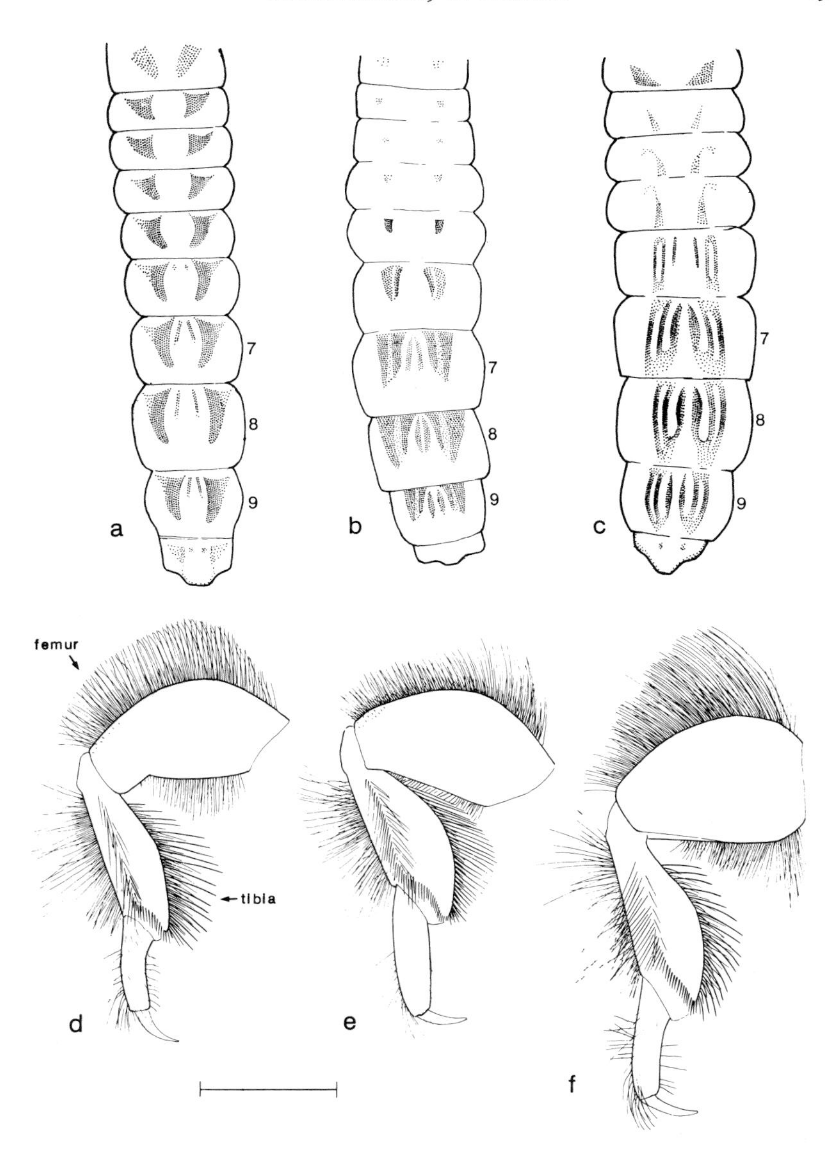


Fig. 34. Ephemeridae: *a-c*, dorsal abdominal patterns of *a*, *Ephemera vulgata*, 16 mm long; *b*, *E. danica*, 15 mm; *c*, *E. lineata*, 15 mm; *d-f*, fore legs of *d*, *E. vulgata*; *e*, *E. danica*; *f*, *E. lineata*. (Scale line 1 mm).

## Family EPHEMERELLIDAE

1 Posterior margins of abdominal tergites with two blunt spines, one on each side of the mid-line (fig. 35*a*); of the four pairs of visible plate-like gills (small 5th pair hidden beneath 4th, see fig. 4*b*), the first three are clearly asymmetrical with an enlarged protuberance on the posterior margin (arrows on fig. 35*c*); pigmentation on gills is similar to the shape of a clover leaf; tails with alternating light and dark bands (fig. 4*b*)— **Ephemerella ignita** (Poda)

Larvae found in fast-flowing streams and rivers, especially where aquatic vegetation is present.

— Posterior margins of abdominal tergites without blunt spines (fig. 35*b*); the four pairs of visible plate-like gills are almost oval in shape and the pigmentation on each gill is also almost oval in shape (fig. 35*d*); tails uniformly pigmented— **Ephemerella notata** Eaton

Larvae found chiefly in moderately fast-flowing rivers.

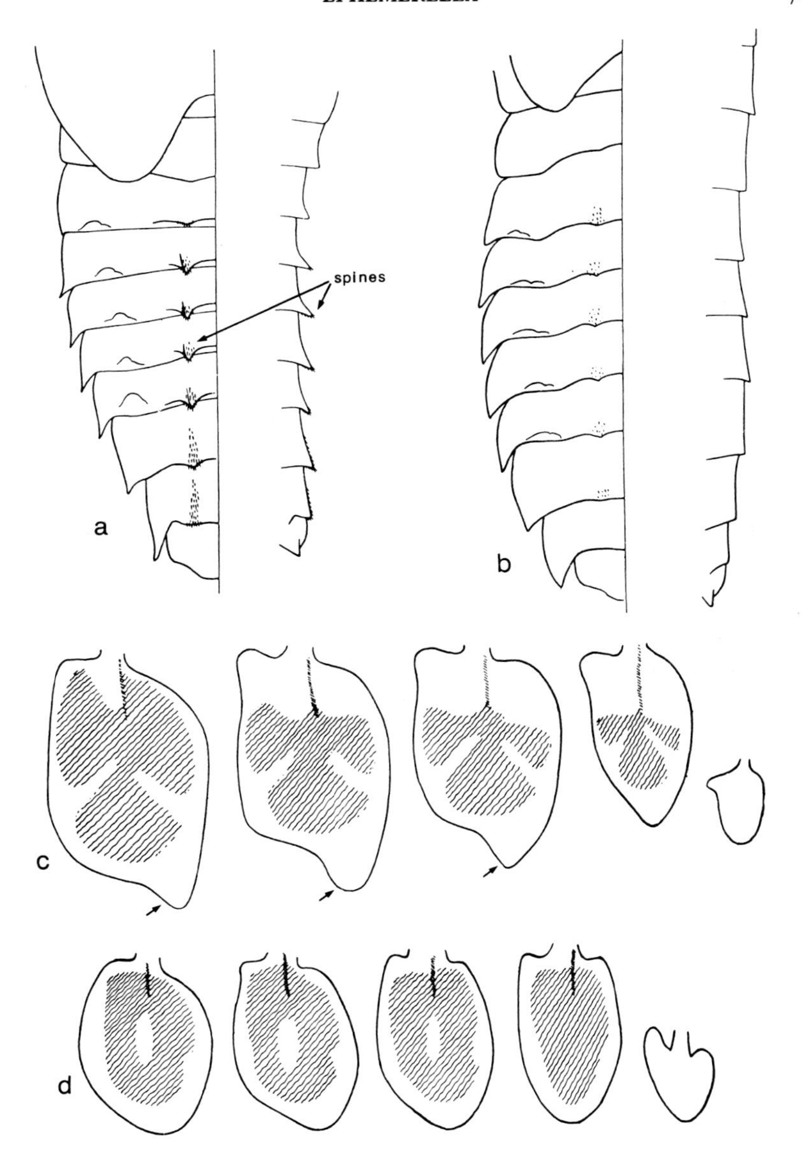


Fig. 35. Ephemerellidae: *a-b*, dorsal view and lateral profile of the abdominal tergites of *a*, *Ephemerella ignita*; *b*, *E. notata*; *c-d*, gills of abdominal segments 3 (left) to 7 of *c*, *E. ignita*; *d*, *E. notata*.

## Family CAENIDAE

1 Head has three prominent ocellar tubercles; lateral margins of abdominal segments 3-7 form broad, flat, bladelike, backwardly-directed projections (fig. 36*a*)— **Brachycercus harrisella** Curtis

Larvae found chiefly in rivers and especially in mud and silt.

— With neither of these characteristics— **2**

2 Lateral margins of pronotum meet the anterior margin to form distinct corners that are approximately right angles; a light median line runs down the head, pronotum and mesonotum; there are usually light dots on the mesonotum (fig. 36*b*); claws are robust and bent at an obtuse angle (fig. 40*a*)— **Caenis robusta** Eaton

The largest British species in the genus *Caenis* with full-grown larvae up to 9 mm long from front of head to tip of abdomen; larvae found chiefly in ponds, rivers and canals, and especially in mud that is rich in organic matter.

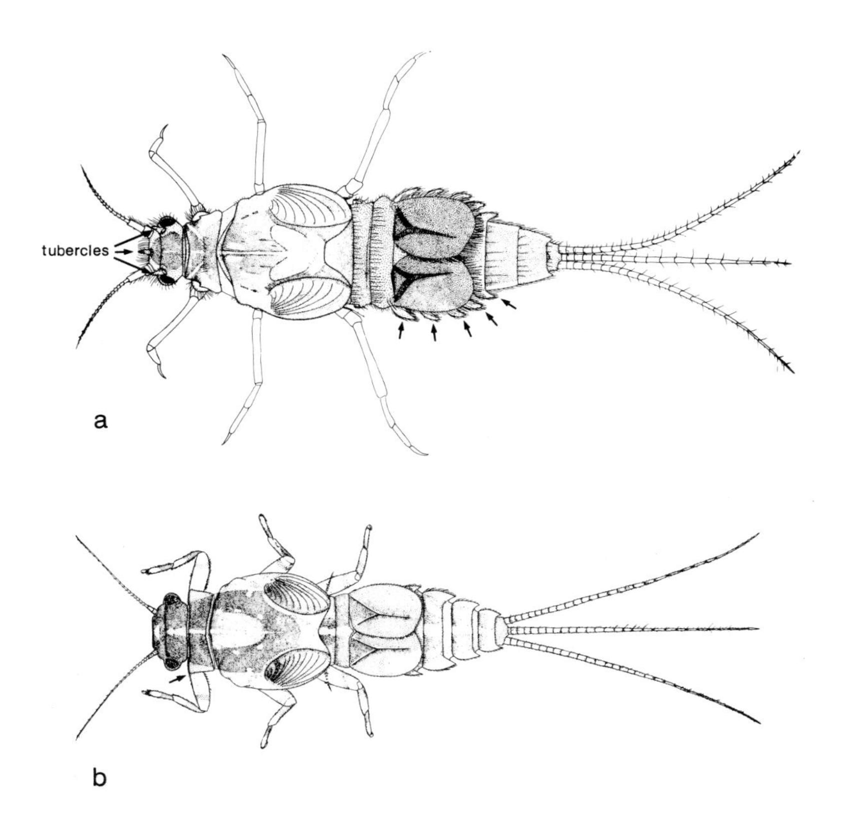


Fig. 36. Caenidae: *a*, *Brachycercus harrisella*, 14 mm long including cerci; *b*, *Caenis robusta*, 15 mm long including cerci.

— Lateral margins of pronotum meet the anterior margin to form a continuous curve; no central light line on the head, pronotum or mesonotum, and no light dots on the latter (figs 37, 40); claws are more slender and only slightly curved (figs 40*b*, *c*, *d*, *e*)— **3**

3 Sides of pronotum diverge outwards towards the anterior margin so that the lateral margins of the pronotum are slightly concave (fig. 37*a*); two small tubercles occur near the mid-line of the pronotum (fig. 37*a*; the tubercles appear as two darkly pigmented dots in fresh specimens but even when the pigment has disappeared in some preserved specimens, the slightly-projecting tubercles can be seen by turning the larva under the microscope; *C. robusta* is the only other species with similar tubercles); last visible sternite of abdomen is broadly truncate without a deep notch in its posterior margin (fig. 38*a*)— **Caenis horaria** (Linnaeus)

Larvae found chiefly in large rivers, canals and lakes, especially in mud and silt.

— Sides of pronotum have straight or slightly convex lateral margins (figs 37*b*, 39); no small tubercles on pronotum; last visible sternite is either broadly truncate (*C. rivulorum*, *C. pusilla*, fig. 38*b*) or has a deep notch in its posterior margin (*C. luctuosa*, *C. macrura*, figs 38*c*, *d*). This character is given here because the pronotum of *C. macrura* and especially *C. luctuosa* is broader towards the anterior (see fig. 39) and therefore these two species could be superficially and erroneously identified as *C. horaria*)— **4**

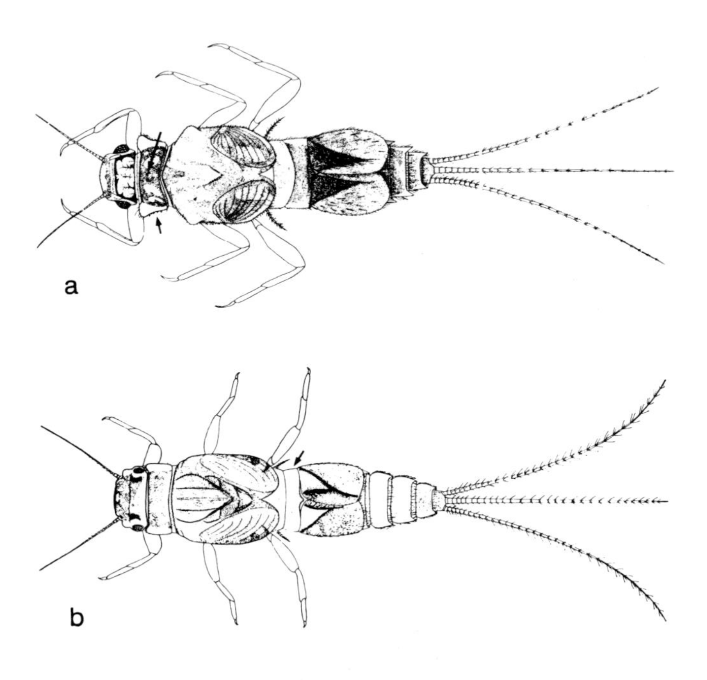


Fig. 37. Caenidae: *a*, *Caenis horaria*, 10 mm long including cerci; *b*, *C. rivulorum*, 5.5 mm long including cerci.

4 Last visible sternite (sternite 9) of abdomen is broadly truncate without a deep notch in its posterior margin (fig. 38*b*); mature larvae (i.e. with well-developed wing buds as in fig. 37*b*) are small (up to 4.5 mm long from front of head to tip of abdomen)— **5**

— Last visible sternite of abdomen has a deep notch in its posterior margin (figs 38*c*, *d*); larvae do not have a pied appearance (figs 39*a*, *b*); mature larvae are medium sized (up to 6.5 mm long from front of head to tip of abdomen)— **6**

5 Lateral margins of the abdominal segments have long, fine bristles (fig. 38*b*); live or recently-preserved larvae have a characteristic pied appearance due to the pale abdominal segments between the thorax and gill covers (fig. 37*b*)— **Caenis rivulorum** Eaton

Larvae found chiefly in stony streams and rivers.

— Lateral margins of the abdominal segments have short, blunt spines (fig. 38*b*); live or recently-preserved larvae do not have a pied appearance and their abdominal segments are uniformly pigmented— **Caenis pusilla** Navas

Single larvae have been recently found in the Candover Brook, a tributary of the River Itchen (Hampshire) (T. Gledhill, personal communication), and in the rivers Wye (Wales) and Frome (Dorset) (Malzacher 1986).

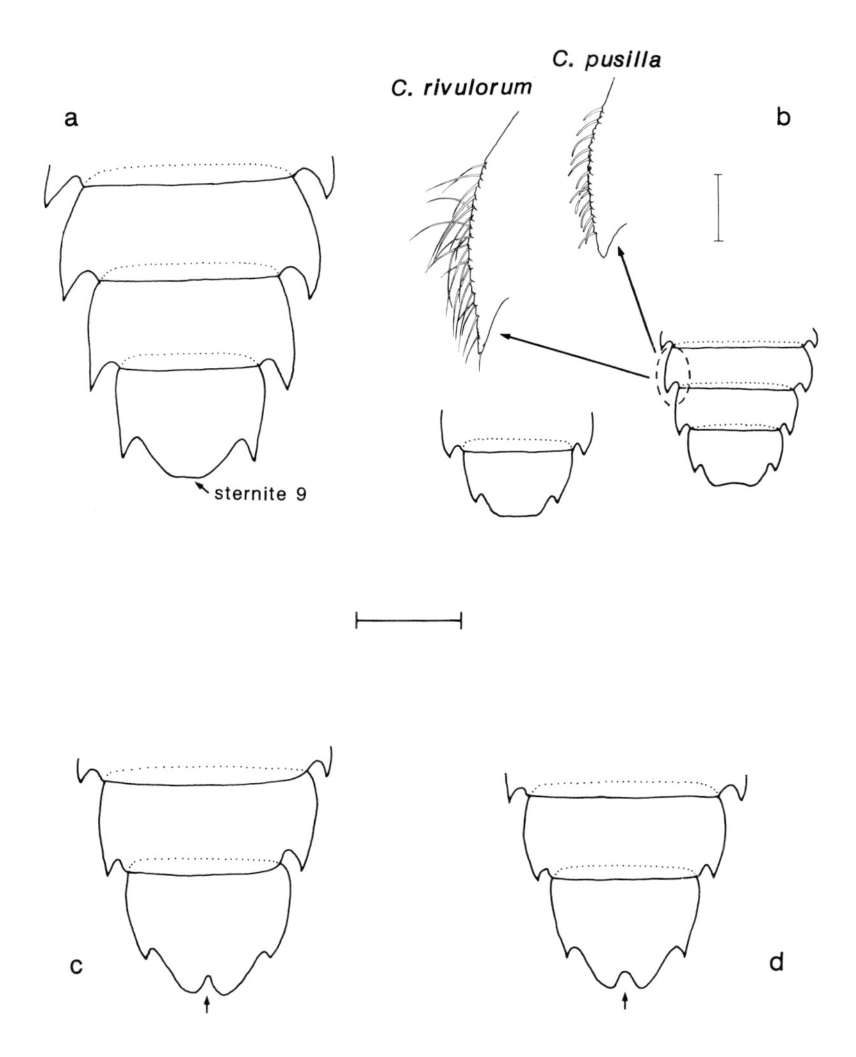


Fig. 38. Caenidae: *a-d*, ventral view of posterior abdominal segments of *a*, *Caenis horaria*; *b*, *C. rivulorum* (showing also bristles on the lateral margin and blunt spines in *C. pusilla*); *c*, *C. luctuosa*; *d*, *C. macrura*. (Scale line 0·5 mm).

6(4) Pronotum is markedly broader near the head (fig. 39*a*); several short, blunt, parallel-sided spines form a straight line transversely across the femur of the fore leg (fig. 40*d*; the spines appear to have bifid tips at a magnification of about 120×); femur usually has a slight concavity on its outer edge (fig. 40*d*); fine hairs cover all the body and fine particles of detritus are often attached to the hairs—
**Caenis luctuosa** (Burmeister)

Larvae found chiefly in rivers, lakes and ponds, and especially amongst silt trapped between gravel and stones.

— Sides of pronotum are usually parallel (fig. 39*b*) but sometimes diverge slightly so that the pronotum is slightly, but never markedly, broader near the head; several long, fine, tapering, hair-like spines form an irregular line across the femur of the fore leg (fig. 40*e*; the spines appear pointed at a magnification of about 120× but at a higher magnification of about 480×, some are seen to have finely frayed and bifid tips); femur has a convex outer edge (fig. 40*e*); fine hairs cover most of the body but are sparse on the thorax—
**Caenis macrura** Stephens

Larvae found chiefly in rivers and especially amongst silt.

(*C. luctuosa* and *C. macrura* can be separated from all other *Caenis* spp. by the deep notch in their last sternite (figs 38*c*, *d*). Unfortunately, it is difficult to separate the two species and none of the above characters are entirely satisfactory. *C. macrura* appears to be the rarer of the two species).

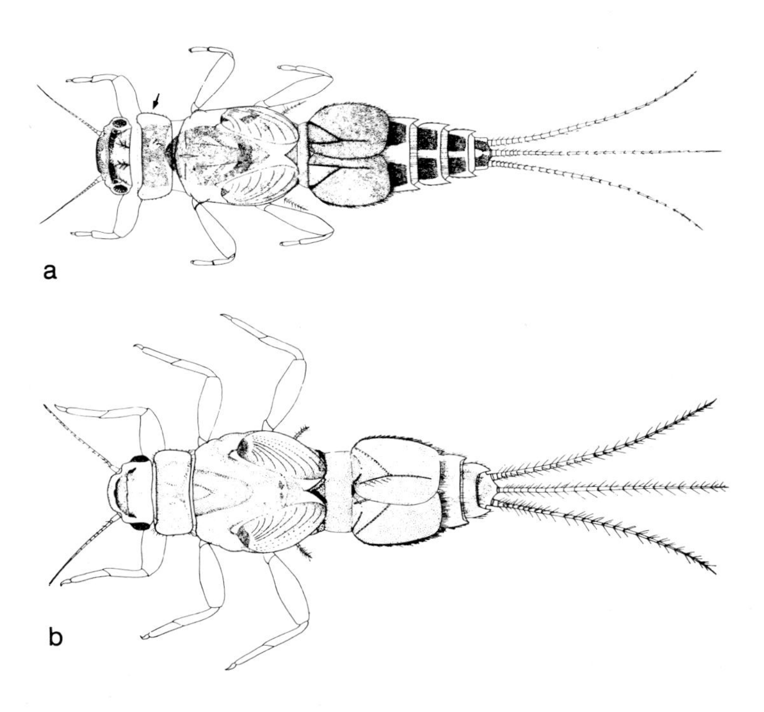


Fig. 39. Caenidae: *a*, *Caenis luctuosa*, 8 mm long including cerci; *b*, *C. macrura*, 7 mm long including cerci.

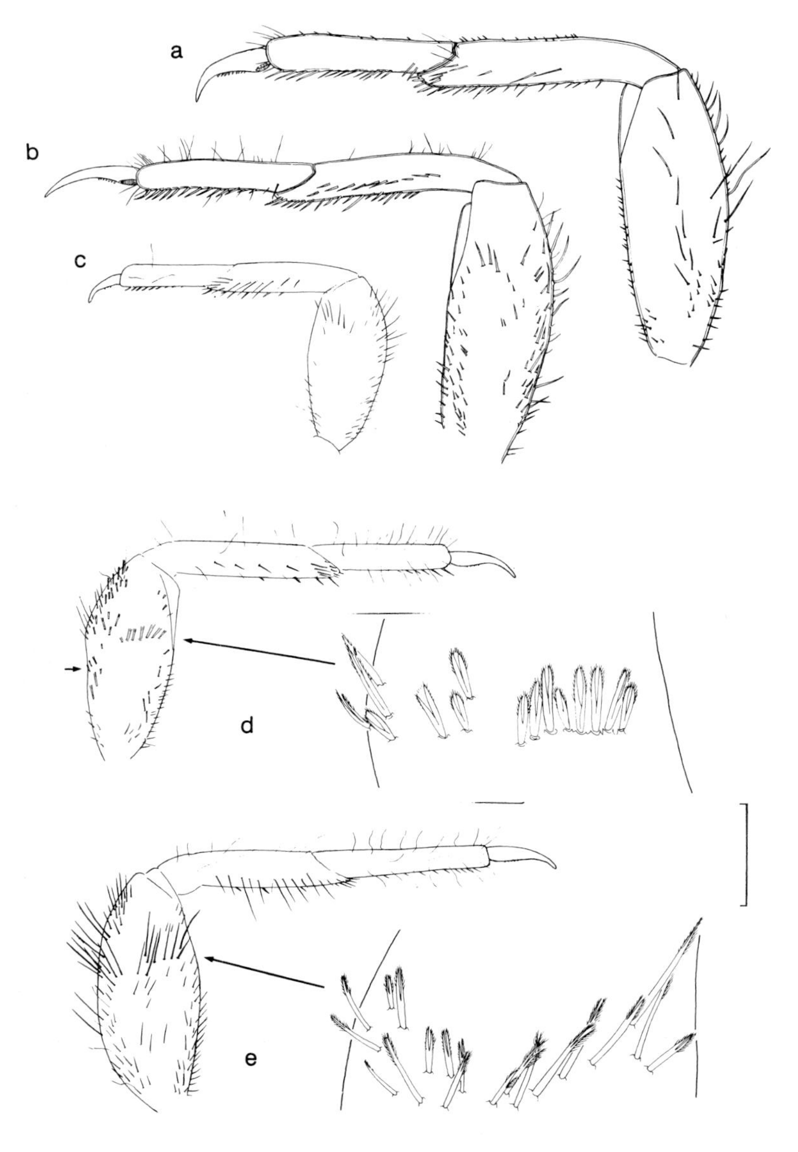


Fig. 40. Caenidae: *a-e*, fore legs of *a*, *Caenis robusta* (femur 1·1 mm long); *b*, *C. horaria*; *c*, *C. rivulorum* (femur 0·45 mm long); *d*, *C. luctuosa* (femur 0·7 mm long); *e*, *C. macrura*.

# ECOLOGY

## HABITATS, HABITS AND FEEDING BEHAVIOUR

This section summarises the habitats in which larvae of Ephemeroptera occur, their general habits and their feeding behaviour. The habitat, habit and feeding classifications are modified versions of those used by other authors (see references in Merritt & Cummins 1978). Information summarised in Tables 2-7 is based largely on our own researches, but we have also used the reviews of others for the sections on feeding behaviour (Cummins 1973; Merritt & Cummins 1978; Soldan 1979; Strenger 1979; Wallace & Merritt 1980; Brittain 1982).

Habitats are divided into running waters (springs, streams, rivers) and standing waters (bogs, ponds, lakes). These two categories are divided in turn into riffles (erosional habitat) and pools/margins (depositional habitats) for running water, and wave-washed shores (erosional habitats) and littoral/profundal zones (depositional habitats) for standing waters. Additional notes on habitats are provided for some species.

The term 'habit' refers to the most obvious behaviour of the larvae, i.e. they can be 'swimmers', 'clingers', 'sprawlers', 'climbers' or 'burrowers'. Swimmers (e.g. figs 4*d*, 5*a*, *b*, *c*) usually have a cylindrical body and long tails fringed with hairs; they cling to submerged stones or plants and usually swim in short bursts. Clingers (e.g. figs 3*d*, 4*a*, *b*) have large, curved, tarsal claws and are usually dorso-ventrally flattened, sometimes with their gills modified to form a ventral sucker (e.g. fig. 26*a*); they can swim if forced to do so. Sprawlers (e.g. figs 3*a*, *c*, 4*c*) live on the surface of leaves of aquatic macrophytes or in the surface layers of fine sediments, especially mud; they are very poor swimmers but often have modifications for maintaining their position on top of the substratum and for ensuring their gills are free of silt. Climbers (e.g. figs 5*a*, *b*) are adapted for moving amongst dense stands of macrophytes, especially on the surface of the stems. Burrowers (e.g. figs 3*b*, 5*d*) live in gravel, sand or mud; they can swim if forced to do so.

Larvae of British Ephemeroptera are all herbivores, feeding chiefly on detritus (decomposing particulate organic matter) and periphyton (attached algae and associated material on the surface of plants and stones). A few species of Ephemeroptera, chiefly in North America but also in South Africa and Malaysia, are omnivores or carnivores (see references in Brittain 1982). Larvae of herbivorous species can be described as 'scrapers', 'collector-filterers', 'collector-gatherers' or 'shredders'. Scrapers feed chiefly on periphyton, collectors either filter or gather chiefly fine detritus (particulate organic matter with a size < 1 mm), and shredders feed chiefly on coarse detritus (decomposing plant tissue or particulate organic matter with a size > 1 mm). None of the British species appears to be a shredder but some North American species in the Ephemerellidae and Leptophlebiidae have been placed in this category (Merritt & Cummins 1978). Species often have to be placed in more than one category because their diet may change with habitat, season and larval development. These changes may simply be a reflection of food availability (Brown 1961a; Kjellberg 1972; McClure & Stewart 1976; Moore 1977; Clifford, Hamilton & Killins 1979; Cianciara 1980; Baekken 1981).

It was not always possible to categorise the British species with certainty and doubts are indicated by question marks in Tables 2-7. The four species in the Siphlonuridae occur in running and standing waters; all are basically swimmers and collector-gatherers (Table 2). Of the fourteen species in the

TABLE 2. HABITATS, HABITS AND FEEDING BEHAVIOUR OF SIPHLONURIDAE

| Species | Habitat | Habit | Feeding behaviour |
|---|---|---|---|
| *Siphlonurus armatus* | Running water (pools/margins) Standing water | Swimmer | Collector-gatherer |
| *S. lacustris* | Running water (pools/margins) Standing water (chiefly ponds at high altitude and lakes) | Swimmer | Collector-gatherer |
| *S. alternatus* | Running water (chiefly deep pools) Standing water (chiefly calcareous lakes) | Swimmer | Collector-gatherer |
| *Ameletus inopinatus* | Running water (chiefly mountain streams) Standing water (highland lochs in Scotland) | Swimmer | Collector-gatherer |

For further information on feeding behaviour, see work on *S. lacustris* (Jones 1950) and the closely-related *S. aestivalis* (Schönmann 1979; Otto & Svensson 1981).

Baetidae, eleven are generally restricted to running water but *Centroptilum luteolum* and the two *Cloeon* spp. occur in running and standing waters; nearly all species are basically swimmers or swimmer-climbers, the exception being the burrowing *Baetis muticus*; the *Baetis* spp. are scrapers and collector-gatherers whereas the remaining species are collector-gatherers (Table 3). Seven of the eleven species in the Heptageniidae occur only in running water but the rest occur in both running and standing waters; all species are basically clingers, scrapers and collector-gatherers (an exception is *Arthroplea congener*, see Table 4). The two *Leptophlebia* spp. in the Leptophlebiidae occur in both running and standing waters but the remaining four species are restricted to running water; the *Leptophlebia* spp. and *Habrophlebia fusca* are sprawler-climbers and the three *Paraleptophlebia* spp. are burrowers; all six species are collector-gatherers (Table 5). All six species in the Potamanthidae, Ephemeridae and Ephemerellidae occur in running water, but *Ephemera danica* and occasionally *Ephemerella ignita* also occur in standing water; the three *Ephemera* spp. are burrowers and collector-filterers, the remaining species are sprawler-clingers and collector-gatherers (Table 6). The seven species in the Caenidae occur in running water but *Caenis luctuosa*, *C. robusta* and *C. horaria* also occur in standing water; all seven species are sprawlers and collector-gatherers (Table 7).

Of the forty-eight British species, thirty occur chiefly in running water, none is restricted to standing water and eighteen occur in both running and standing waters. Seventeen species are basically swimmers, eleven are clingers, thirteen are sprawlers and seven are burrowers. The majority of species are collector-gatherers (twenty-six) or scrapers and collector-gatherers (eighteen), and only four are collector-filterers.

Although some information can be provided on feeding behaviour, little is known about the fraction of the food intake that is actually digested and absorbed. Two European species in the Leptophlebiidae, *Habroleptoides modesta* and *Habrophlebia lauta*, are apparently coprophagous (eat their own faeces) and this may increase digestion efficiency (Pleskot 1953). Although there is negligible cellulase activity in Ephemeroptera larvae (Monk 1976), damaged algae may leak organic compounds that provide nourishment (Cummins 1973). The proteolytic activity of trypsin- and pepsin-like enzymes is high in larvae of Ephemeroptera (Dabrowski & Glogowski 1977), and these enzymes may facilitate the digestion of fungi and bacteria. However, Baker & Bradnam (1976) found no evidence for digestion of bacteria in the guts of *Ephemerella ignita* and *Baetis* spp. There is clearly an urgent need for more work on nutrition in larvae of Ephemeroptera.

## TABLE 3. HABITATS, HABITS AND FEEDING BEHAVIOUR OF BAETIDAE

| Species | Habitat | Habit | Feeding behaviour |
|---|---|---|---|
| *Baetis fuscatus* and *B. scambus* | Running water (chiefly on macrophytes and on sand/gravel) | Swimmer and climber | Scraper and collector-gatherer |
| *B. vernus* | Running water (mountain streams, pools/margins and on macrophytes of rivers) | Swimmer | Scraper and collector-gatherer |
| *B. buceratus* | Running water (chiefly rivers) | Swimmer | Scraper and collector-gatherer |
| *B. rhodani* | Running water (chiefly riffles) | Swimmer | Scraper and collector-gatherer |
| *B. atrebatinus* | Running water (chiefly calcareous?) | Swimmer | Scraper and collector-gatherer |
| *B. muticus* | Running water (chiefly riffles) | Burrower | Scraper-gatherer (scraper?) |
| *B. niger* and *B. digitatus* | Running water (chiefly on macrophytes) | Swimmer and climber | Scraper and collector-gatherer |
| *Centroptilum luteolum* | Running water (pools/margins and on macrophytes)<br>Standing water (wave-washed shores) | Swimmer and climber | Collector-gatherer |
| *C. pennulatum* | Running water (pools/margins and on macrophytes) | Swimmer and climber | Collector-gatherer |
| *Cloeon dipterum* | Running water (pools/margins and on macrophytes)<br>Standing water (eutrophic ponds and shallow water in lakes) | Swimmer and climber | Collector-gatherer |
| *C. simile* | Running water (pools/margins and on macrophytes)<br>Standing water (on macrophytes in deep water) | Swimmer and climber | Collector-gatherer |
| *Procloeon bifidum* | Running water (pools/margins and on macrophytes) | Swimmer and climber | Collector-gatherer |

For further information on feeding behaviour, see work on *B. rhodani* (Jones 1950; Brown 1961a; Larsen 1978; Bohle 1978; Baekken 1981; Klonowska 1986), *C. luteolum* (Klonowska 1986), *C. dipterum* (Brown 1960, 1961a; Cianciara 1980).

TABLE 4. HABITATS, HABITS AND FEEDING BEHAVIOUR OF HEPTAGENIIDAE

| Species | Habitat | Habit | Feeding behaviour |
|---|---|---|---|
| *Rhithrogena semicolorata* | Running water (chiefly riffles) | Clinger | Scraper and collector-gatherer |
| *R. germanica* | Running water (chiefly riffles in large rivers) | Clinger | Scraper and collector-gatherer |
| *Heptagenia sulphurea* | Running water (chiefly riffles in large rivers) Standing water (wave-washed shores of calcareous lakes) | Clinger and swimmer | Scraper and collector-gatherer |
| *H. longicauda* | Running water (riffles in large rivers) | Clinger and swimmer | Scraper and collector-gatherer |
| *H. fuscogrisea* | Running water (riffles and on macrophytes?) Standing water (wave-washed shores and macrophytes of calcareous lakes) | Clinger and swimmer | Scraper and collector-gatherer |
| *H. lateralis* | Running water (chiefly riffles) Standing water (wave-washed shores) | Clinger and swimmer | Scraper and collector-gatherer |
| *Arthroplea congener* | Running water (pools/margins) | Clinger and swimmer | Collector-filterer |
| *Ecdyonurus venosus* and *E. torrentis* | Running water (chiefly riffles) | Clinger and swimmer | Scraper and collector-gatherer |
| *E. dispar* | Running water (chiefly riffles) Standing water (wave-washed shores) | Clinger and swimmer | Scraper and collector-gatherer |
| *E. insignis* | Running water (chiefly riffles in rivers) | Clinger and swimmer | Scraper and collector-gatherer |

For further information on feeding behaviour, see work on *Rhithrogena* spp. and *Ecdyonurus* spp. (Strenger 1953, 1979), *E. venosus* (Moore 1977; Klonowska 1986), *A. congener* (Froehlich 1964; Soldán 1979), *R. semicolorata* and *H. lateralis* (Jones 1950).

TABLE 5. HABITATS, HABITS AND FEEDING BEHAVIOUR OF LEPTOPHLEBIIDAE

| Species | Habitat | Habit | Feeding behaviour |
|---|---|---|---|
| *Leptophlebia marginata* and *L. vespertina* | Running water (pools/margins and on macrophytes)<br>Standing water (chiefly on macrophytes) | Sprawler and climber | Collector-gatherer |
| *Paraleptophlebia submarginata* and *P. cincta*(?) | Running water (pools/margins and on bryophytes) | Burrower | Collector-gatherer |
| *P. werneri* | Running water (pools/margins and on macrophytes, chiefly calcareous streams) | Burrower | Collector-gatherer |
| *Habrophlebia fusca* | Running water (pools/margins and on macrophytes) | Sprawler and climber | Collector-gatherer |

For further information on feeding behaviour, see work on *L. vespertina* (Kjellberg 1972) and *P. submarginata* (Pleskot 1953).

TABLE 6. HABITATS, HABITS AND FEEDING BEHAVIOUR OF POTAMANTHIDAE, EPHEMERIDAE AND EPHEMERELLIDAE

| Species | Habitat | Habit | Feeding behaviour |
|---|---|---|---|
| *Potamanthus luteus* | Running water (pools/margins) | Sprawler and clinger | Collector-gatherer |
| *Ephemera vulgata* | Running water (pools/margins, chiefly in mud) | Burrower | Collector-filterer |
| *E. danica* | Running water (pools/margins, chiefly in sand/gravel)<br>Standing water (chiefly in sand/gravel) | Burrower | Collector-filterer |
| *E. lineata* | Running water (pools/margins, large rivers) | Burrower | Collector-filterer |
| *Ephemerella ignita* and *E. notata* | Running water (on stones and macrophytes) (*E. ignita* occasionally on stony shores of lakes) | Clinger and sprawler | Collector-gatherer |

For further information on feeding behaviour, see work on *E. danica* (Strenger 1973, 1975; Moore 1977; Otto & Svensson 1981; Klonowska 1986), *E. notata* (Jones 1950).

TABLE 7. HABITATS, HABITS AND FEEDING BEHAVIOUR OF CAENIDAE

| Species | Habitat | Habit | Feeding behaviour |
|---|---|---|---|
| *Brachycercus harrisella* | Running water (pools/margins, chiefly in mud/silt) | Sprawler | Collector-gatherer |
| *Caenis macrura* | Running water (pools/margins of rivers, chiefly in silt) | Sprawler | Collector-gatherer |
| *C. luctuosa* | Running water (pools/margins of rivers, chiefly in silt)<br>Standing water (chiefly in silt between gravel and stones) | Sprawler | Collector-gatherer |
| *C. robusta* | Running water (pools/margins of rivers, chiefly in mud)<br>Standing water (chiefly in mud of ponds, canals) | Sprawler | Collector-gatherer |
| *C. horaria* | Running water (pools/margins of rivers, chiefly in mud)<br>Standing water (chiefly in mud/silt of lakes, canals) | Sprawler | Collector-gatherer |
| *C. rivulorum* and *C. pusilla*? | Running water (pools/margins of stony streams and rivers) | Sprawler | Collector-gatherer |

## EGG HATCHING

Information on adult emergence, flight period, flight behaviour, mating, fecundity, oviposition behaviour and egg development was summarised by Elliott & Humpesch (1983). Quantitative information on egg hatching is available for only eight of the forty-eight British species (Table 8). Most species hatch within the range 3-21°C, but *Baetis rhodani* has a higher upper limit of 25°C whilst the lower limit is between 4·5°C (no hatching) and 5·9°C (4-11% hatching) in *Rhithrogena semicolorata*. The maximum percentage of eggs hatching in the laboratory is over 90% for the two *Baetis* spp. and *Ephemerella ignita*, but is always less than 50% for *R. semicolorata* and the four *Ecdyonurus* spp. This low hatching success probably occurs in the field and must be taken into account in the interpretation of life

TABLE 8. INFORMATION ON EGG HATCHING FOR EPHEMEROPTERA SPECIES OCCURRING IN BRITAIN

Approximate temperature range over which eggs hatched, mean values for the maximum percentage of eggs that hatched, equation relating hatching time to temperature, whether or not equation has been tested in the field, and mean number (with 95% CL) of days for 50% of the eggs to hatch at 5°C and 10°C.

| Species | *T*°C | Max % hatched | Equation | Tested in field | Days for 50% hatch | | Reference |
|---|---|---|---|---|---|---|---|
| | | | | | at 5°C | at 10°C | |
| *B. vernus* | 6.8-20.0 | >94 | hyperbola (prediapause) (postdiapause) exponential (diapause) | no | | | 2a,6 |
| *Baetis rhodani* | 3.0-25.0 | 99 | power-function | yes | 66(64-68) | 26(25-27) | 1,2a,3a |
| *Rhithrogena semicolorata* | 5.9-19.9 | 28 | power-function | yes | 154(148-160) | 41(40-42) | 5 |
| *E. venosus* | 3.6-20.6 | 48 | power-function | no | 166(157-176) | 45(43-47) | 4 |
| *E. torrentis* | 3.9-19.6 | 29 | power-function | no | 138(124-154) | 39(37-41) | 4 |
| *Ecdyonurus dispar* (lakes) | 3.9-20.3 | 38 | power-function | yes | 180(170-191) | 52(50-54) | 4 |
| (rivers) | 4.4-20.1 | 21 | not known | | | | 4 |
| *E. insignis* | 8.7-19.9 | 13 | power-function | no | — | 48(47-49) | 4 |
| *Ephemerella ignita* | 5.9-19.8 | >90 | hyperbola | yes | 603(526-744) | 134(117-165) | 2b,3b |

References: 1, Benech 1972a; 2, Bohle, a 1969, b 1972; 3, Elliott, a 1972, b 1978; 4, Humpesch 1980a; 5, Humpesch & Elliott 1980; 6, Schmidt 1984.

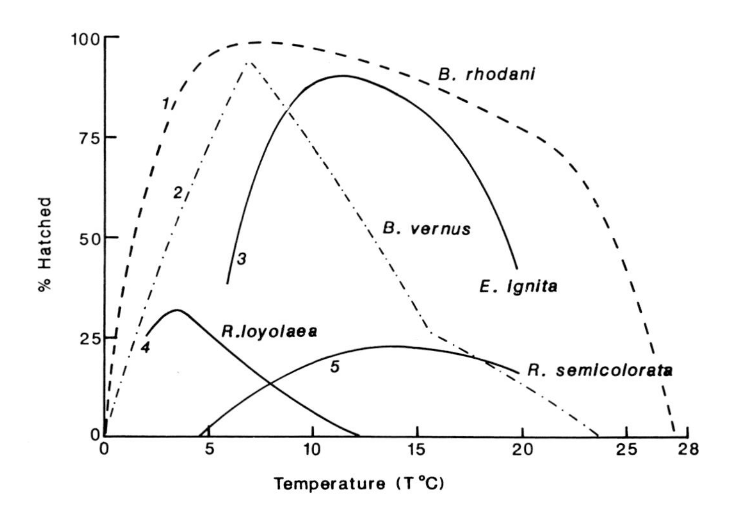


Fig. 41. Comparison of the percentages of eggs hatching at each temperature for European species of Ephemeroptera: 1, *Baetis rhodani* (combined data; Bohle 1969; Elliott 1972; Benech 1972a); 2, *B. vernus* (Bohle 1969); 3, *Ephemerella ignita* (Elliott 1978); 4, *Rhithrogena loyolaea*; 5, *R. semicolorata* (Humpesch & Elliott 1980).

cycles and population dynamics. There is a clear relationship between hatching success and water temperature in some species (fig. 41), but not in *Ecdyonurus* spp. The Central European species, *R. loyolaea*, is included in fig. 41 as an example of a species with a very narrow range of temperature for hatching.

The relationship between hatching time ($Y$ days after oviposition or fertilization) and water temperature ($T$°C) could not be described by an equation in four populations, two of which had a diapause (diapause is a period of suspended development or growth with a greatly decreased metabolism) in the egg stage; one population of *Baetis vernus* and *Ephemerella ignita* (Bohle 1969, 1972). In all other populations, the relationship has been well described by a hyperbola or a power function, e.g. British species in Table 8. Both models are summarized by a general equation [$Y = a/(T\text{-}t)^b$] where $a$, $b$ and $t$ are constants. If $t = 0$, then the equation is a two-parameter power function ($Y = aT^{-b}$). If $b = 1$ and $t$ is the threshold temperature at which the development rate is theoretically zero, then the equation is identical to the two-parameter hyperbolic curve [$Y = a/(T\text{-}t)$]

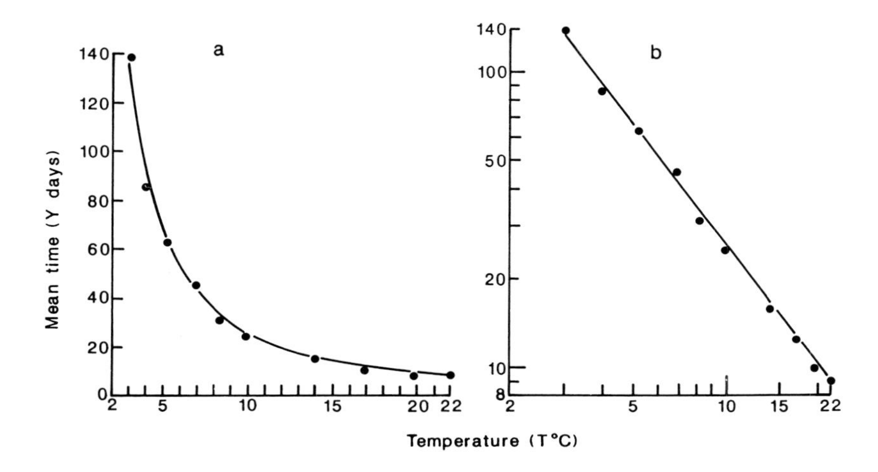


Fig. 42. Relationship between the mean time required ($Y$ days) for 50% of the eggs of *B. rhodani* to hatch and temperature ($T$°C) in the laboratory: *a*, on arithmetic scale with curvilinear regression line; *b*, on log/log scale with linear regression line.

with the constant, $a$, equal to the number of degree-days above $t$ °C required for hatching. The general equation has been successfully fitted to data for ten species and fifteen populations of European Ephemeroptera, including seven species occurring in Britain. A hyperbolic curve was the best model for *E. ignita* and a power function was more suitable for the remaining six species (Table 8). An example of the good fit of the power function is given in fig. 42. The exception is *B. vernus* in which the embryonic development is divided into three stages; prediapause, diapause, postdiapause. The durations of the first and third stages have been described by a hyperbola and the diapause stage by an exponential relationship (Schmidt 1984).

The usefulness of the models increases considerably if they can be used to predict the time of hatching in the field. This has now been tested successfully for six species, including four British species (Table 8). Hatching times vary considerably between species, e.g. values for 50% of eggs to hatch at 5°C and 10°C (Table 8). Hatching times are remarkably similar for different populations of some species; e.g., *Baetis rhodani* from France (Benech 1972a) and England (Elliott 1972), *Ecdyonurus dispar* from two streams in England (Humpesch 1980a) and *Rhithrogena semicolorata* from two streams in England (Humpesch & Elliott 1980). They can also vary considerably between populations of the same species; e.g. *E. dispar* from lakes and rivers (Humpesch 1980a), *E. venosus* from streams in Austria and England (Humpesch 1980a) and *Ephemerella ignita* from streams in France, Germany and England with an obligatory diapause in the eggs of the German population (Thibault 1969; Bohle 1972; Elliott 1978). These differences may be genuine but it is also possible that the work was done on different species that were not recognized because of taxonomic inadequacies. The latter was not the case for *E. dispar* from lakes and rivers because an electrophoretic study showed that there were no monomorphic enzyme-loci that differed between the three populations (Hefti, Humpesch & Tonka 1988).

It has also been shown that in two *Ecdyonurus* spp. and one *Rhithrogena* sp., both the hatching time and rate of development are similar for constant and fluctuating temperatures (Humpesch 1982). Once the eggs start to hatch, the period over which most eggs hatch may be remarkably short in some species, e.g. less than ten days for *Rhithrogena* spp., *Baetis rhodani* (if $T>5°C$), and *Ecdyonurus* spp. (if $T>10°C$) (Elliott 1972; Humpesch 1980a; Humpesch & Elliott 1980). Tiny larvae of these species occur over several months and this observation has often been interpreted as an indication of a long hatching period. It is now obvious that this interpretation is incorrect and therefore the most likely explanation is that some larvae grow very slowly after hatching. This is one example of the value of information on hatching times, and it emphasizes the importance of this information for the interpretation of life cycles.

Eggs can develop parthenogenetically (i.e. without fertilization) in many species. Parthenogenesis was recorded by Degrange (1960) in twenty-six European species, fourteen of which occur in Britain, namely: *Caenis luctuosa, Ephemerella ignita, Ecdyonurus insignis, E. dispar, Heptagenia lateralis, H. sulphurea, Leptophlebia vespertina, Siphlonurus lacustris, Centroptilum luteolum, C. pennulatum, Cloeon simile, Baetis niger, B. muticus, B. scambus*. Hirvenoja (1964) also recorded parthenogensis in *Cloeon simile*. Humpesch (1980b) found that eggs can develop parthenogenetically in five species of *Ecdyonurus* and two species of *Rhithrogena*, including the British species *E. dispar, E. insignis, E. torrentis* and *E. venosus*. For the last two species and for the Central European species, *E. picteti*, there were sufficient data to show that the relationship between hatching time and water temperature was well described by a power function. As males are known for all the European species, the parthenogenesis is not obligatory. When comparisons were made between the development of fertilized and unfertilized (parthenogenetic) eggs, the latter took longer to develop and fewer of them hatched (Degrange 1960; Humpesch 1980b). In some species (e.g. *Cloeon simile*) the unfertilized eggs produced only females, whilst in other species (e.g. *Centroptilum luteolum*) males were also produced but only in low numbers.

Ovoviviparity is rare in the Ephemeroptera and is restricted to the Baetidae. In Europe, *Cloeon dipterum* is the only species known to be ovoviviparous (Degrange 1959a). The female imago rests for 10-14 days after copulation and then lays her eggs on the water surface. As soon as the eggs come into contact with the water, they hatch and the larvae swim away. Some authors claim that the eggs can hatch inside the abdomen of the female, but this is unlikely (see review by Degrange 1959a).

## LARVAL GROWTH

Ephemeroptera have a large number of postembyronic moults and various methods have been used to determine the number of instars (see review by Fink 1980); (an 'instar' is the development stage between two moults). The number of larval instars is known for several species (Humpesch 1979), including the British species *Baetis vernus* (Illies & Masteller 1977; Schmidt 1984), *Cloeon dipterum* (Cianciara 1979), *C. simile* (Degrange 1959b), *Ecdyonurus dispar* (Humpesch 1981), and *Leptophlebia vespertina* (Brittain 1976). Estimates vary from ten to fifty but the majority of species are in the range of twenty to thirty larval instars.

Growth patterns of larval Ephemeroptera reflect the interaction between the size increment per moult and the moulting frequency. Both variables are affected by many factors, including temperature, food, water chemistry and larval activity. As information on these interactions is sparse, the following example is given, but it must be emphasised that it may not be typical of other species. In *Ecdyonurus dispar*, the average body length increment per moult is fairly constant at about 15% (fig. 43) and therefore Dyar's rule is applicable (Humpesch 1981). As smaller mature larvae have fewer instars than larger mature larvae, the number of instars between egg hatching and adult emergence is not constant. Temperature is the chief variable affecting the interval between moults and this relationship is well described by a power function for *E. dispar*, with the moulting interval varying from 28 days at 5°C to only 4 days at 20°C. Some authors have suggested that the moulting interval also changes with larval age but no reliable data are available. Unlike other aquatic insects, none of the Ephemeroptera has been found to have a larval diapause (a diapause does occur in the eggs of some species, see page 90).

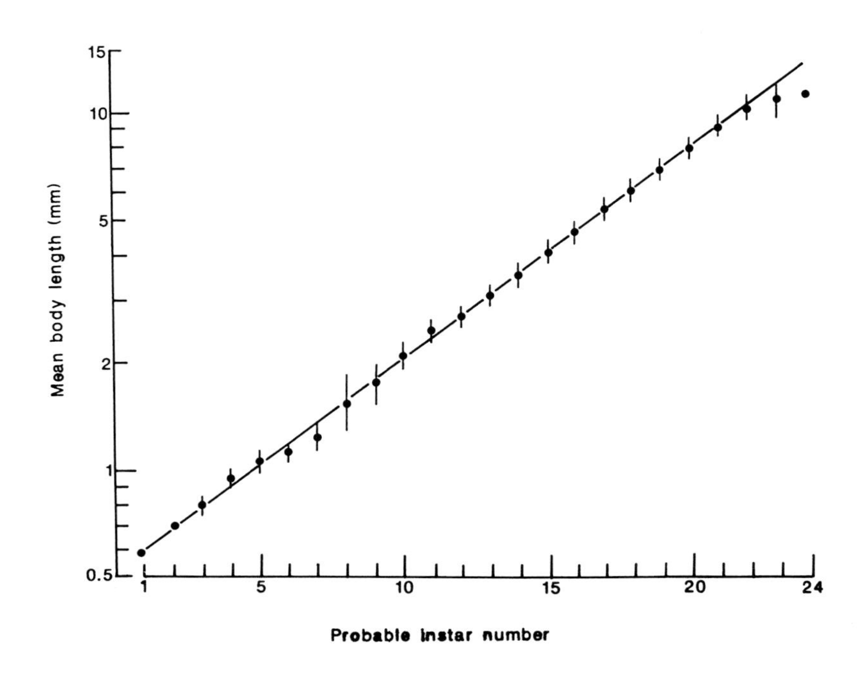


Fig. 43. Relationship between mean body length ($Y$ mm) and instar number ($X$) for *Ecdyonurus dispar* reared in the laboratory (regression line: $\ln Y = 0{\cdot}135 \ln X - 0{\cdot}635$).

Estimates of larval growth rates are available for only eight of the British species (Table 9). As growth is approximately exponential for long periods, specific growth rates for body length ($G_L$% day$^{-1}$) can be estimated and compared. They range from close to zero in winter to 3·26% day$^{-1}$ in summer (Table 9). As growth rates are generally higher in summer than winter, temperature is the most obvious factor responsible for the differences. Its effect on growth rates was clearly demonstrated for cohorts of *Baetis rhodani* in the field (fig. 44) and for *Ecdyonurus dispar* reared in the laboratory at constant temperatures, growth rates for body length being 0·38% day$^{-1}$ at *c.* 4°C, 0·76% day$^{-1}$ at *c.* 9°C, 1·56% day$^{-1}$ at *c.* 14°C and 3·55% day$^{-1}$ at 20°C (Humpesch 1981).

TABLE 9. INFORMATION ON GROWTH RATES FOR EPHEMEROPTERA SPECIES OCCURRING IN BRITAIN

Locality where larvae of each species occurred, approximate water temperature range in °C, duration of life cycle in months from egg hatching to adult emergence, number of cohorts present during the year and the range of specific growth rates for body length ($G_L$% day$^{-1}$).

| Species | Locality | $T$°C | Duration of life cycle (months) | Cohorts | $G_L$ summer | $G_L$ winter | Reference |
|---|---|---|---|---|---|---|---|
| *Baetis rhodani* | Experimental stream | 8.1-16.3 | 2-5 | 7 | 1.58-2.45 | 1.07-1.38 | 1 |
| | Unterseebach (Austria) | 1.2-21.0 | 2.5-8 | 4 | 2.33-3.01 | 0.65-2.97 | 2a |
| *Centroptilum luteolum* | Experimental stream | 8.1-15.1 | 3-8 | 3? | 0.63 | 0.09 | 1 |
| *Ecdyonurus dispar* | Laboratory | 3.0-21.1 | 3 at 20°C | — | 0.23-4.16 | | 2b |
| | Windermere | 11.1-15.3 | 12 | 1 | | 1.25-1.60 | 2b |
| *Leptophlebia vespertina* | Llyn Dinas | *c.* 2.0-*c.* 24.0 | 12 | 1 | 0.39-1.36 | | 3 |
| | Oak Mere | *c.* 0-24.0 | 12 | 1 | 0.00-2.94 | | 4 |
| *Paraleptophlebia submarginata* | Experimental stream | 8.1-16.8 | 7 | ? | 1.17 | 0.19 | 1 |
| *Ephemera danica* | Stampen (Sweden) | 0.8-14.6 | 24-36 | 4 | 0.00-0.70 | | 5 |
| *Ephemerella ignita* | Experimental stream | 9.7-15.1 | 5 | 1 | 3.26 | — | 1 |
| *Caenis rivulorum* | Experimental stream | 9.1-16.8 | 11 | 1 | — | 0.87 | 1 |

References: 1, Welton, Ladle & Bass 1982; 2, Humpesch, a 1979, b 1981; 3, Brittain 1976; 4, Savage 1986; 5, Svensson 1977.

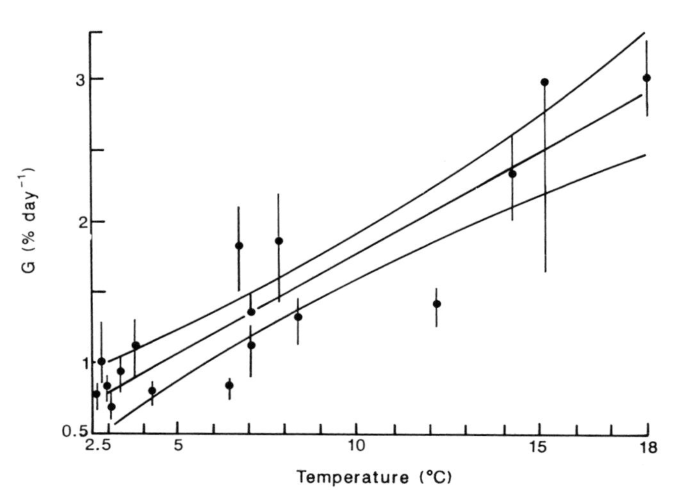


Fig. 44. Relationship between specific growth rate for body length ($G_L$% day$^{-1}$±95% CL) of *Baetis rhodani* cohorts in the field and mean water temperature ($T$°C) (regression line: $G_L = 0{\cdot}35 + 0{\cdot}14T$).

Some of the variations in growth rates at similar temperatures (e.g. fig. 44) may be due to variations in food quality and quantity. For example, the larval stage of *Cloeon dipterum* was completed in 147 days on a diet of detritus and 211 days on a diet of the alga *Spirogyra* sp. (Cianciara 1980).

Information on fecundity and number of eggs laid (Elliott & Humpesch 1983), egg hatching success, larval mortality and adult density can be used to construct life tables for Ephemeroptera. Unfortunately, there is only one detailed study for a European species, namely *Ephemerella major* (Rosillon 1986a). For one cohort in a Belgian stream, the mean fecundity was 1,365 eggs per female, there were 30 ovipositing females per m$^2$ and therefore 40,950 eggs were laid per m$^2$. Four months after hatching, larval density had decreased to 2,090 per m$^2$ and this decrease continued so that there were 450 larvae per m$^2$ just before adult emergence commenced. Adult density was estimated at 210 per m$^2$ (50% females) and 55 females survived to lay eggs at the start of the next cohort. Over 95% of the mortality occurred in the egg stage and early larval instars, and less than 0·5% of the eggs developed through to the adult stage. This low percentage was sufficient to ensure the survival of the population; the compensating factor was probably the high fecundity. In the case of the North American burrowing species *Hexagenia limbata*, only 0·02% of the eggs developed through to the adult stage (Horst 1976). There is clearly a need for more information on the life tables of British Ephemeroptera.

## BIOMASS AND PRODUCTION

Various methods can be used to estimate production, provided that estimates of growth rates, mortality rates and biomass are available (see reviews of methodology by Waters 1977; Downing & Rigler 1984). Estimates of mean biomass and production are available for twelve species on the British list but some of these estimates are for non-British populations (Table 10). The estimates have been converted to common units (g dry weight per $m^2$), using the allometric relationships between wet weight and length (wet weight $= a$ length$^b$, where $a$ and $b$ are constants) and between dry weight and length (dry weight $= c$ length$^d$, where $c$ and $d$ are constants).

The first exponent, $b$, varies in the range 2·09-3·74, values for individual species being 2·88 for *Baetis rhodani* (Zelinka & Marvan 1976), 3·53-3·74 for *Cloeon dipterum* (Cianciara 1979), 2·57 for *Rhithrogena semicolorata* (Zelinka & Marvan 1976), and 2·09-2·12 for *Leptophlebia vespertina* (Brittain 1978). The second exponent, $d$, has been given a general value of 2·88 for larvae of Ephemeroptera (Smock 1980), values for individual species being 3·63-3·73 for *C. dipterum* (Cianciara 1979), 3·00-3·55 for *L. vespertina* (Brittain 1978; Savage 1986), and 2·86 for *Ephemera danica* (Svensson 1977). Dry weight is expressed as a percentage of wet weight by some workers, values being 20·1% for *B. rhodani* (Zelinka 1984), 21·8-23·7% for *C. dipterum* (Cianciara 1979), 24·5% for *R. semicolorata* (Zelinka 1984), 22·8% for *Ecdyonurus venosus* (Zelinka 1984) and 9·5-13·1% for *L. vespertina* (Brittain 1978).

Estimates of annual production (g dry weight per $m^2$) vary from only 0·2 g for *Caenis macrura* to 5·8 g for *Baetis rhodani* (Table 10). There is a similar large variation in mean biomass (0·02-3·6 g dry weight per $m^2$) and the ratio of production to mean biomass (1·6-16·1). The latter ratio ($P/\bar{B}$) was calculated on an annual basis for the values in Table 10 and therefore does not take into account the length of the life cycle. *Ephemera danica*, with a life cycle taking longer than one year, has the lowest $P/\bar{B}$ ratio. Most annual species appear to have a $P/\bar{B}$ ratio in the range 4-9, and species with more than one generation per year have a $P/\bar{B}$ ratio higher than 9 (e.g. *Baetis* spp. and *Cloeon dipterum*). These generalizations cannot be confirmed until more information is available and, once again, more work is needed on the British species.

TABLE 10. INFORMATION ON ANNUAL MEAN BIOMASS ($\bar{B}$, g dry weight per m$^2$), ANNUAL PRODUCTION ($P$, g dry weight per m$^2$) AND $P/\bar{B}$ RATIO FOR EPHEMEROPTERA SPECIES OCCURRING IN BRITAIN.

| Species | $\bar{B}$ (g m$^{-2}$) | $P$ (g m$^{-2}$) | $P/\bar{B}$ | Reference |
|---|---|---|---|---|
| *Baetis fuscatus* | 0.029 | 0.320 | 11.04 | 1a |
| *B. scambus* | 0.03 | 0.11-0.12 | 4.17-4.63 | 9 |
| *B. buceratus* | 0.113 | 1.330 | 11.77 | 1a |
| *B. rhodani* | 0.133 | 1.063 | 8.00 | 1b |
| | 0.299 | 2.081 | 9.09 | 1c |
| | 0.76-0.79 | 5.61-5.83 | 7.40 | 2 |
| | 0.17 | 1.12-1.37 | 6.38-7.85 | 9 |
| *Cloeon dipterum* | 0.084 | 0.936 | 11.14 | 1a |
| *Rhithrogena semicolorata* | 0.345 | 3.045 | 8.83 | 1b |
| | 0.455 | 4.335 | 9.53 | 1c |
| | 0.103 | 0.433 | 4.21 | 3 |
| | 0.115 | 0.738 | 6.40 | 8 |
| | 0.12 | 0.59-0.68 | 4.76-5.54 | 9 |
| *Ecdyonurus venosus* | 0.070 | 0.663 | 9.47 | 1a |
| *Leptophlebia vespertina* | — | 0.76-1.22 | — | 7 |
| *Potamanthus luteus* | 0.017 | 0.186 | 10.92 | 4 |
| | 0.128 | 2.064 | 16.13 | 5 |
| | 0.078 | 0.571 | 7.32 | 1a |
| *Ephemera danica* | 3.57 | 5.58 | 1.56 | 6 |
| *Ephemerella ignita* | 0.096 | 0.635 | 6.62 | 3 |
| | 0.104 | 1.147 | 11.03 | 1a |
| | 0.927-1.073 | 3.8-4.4 | 4.1 | 2 |
| | 0.083 | 0.584 | 7.0 | 8 |
| | 0.26 | 1.23-1.36 | 4.69-5.18 | 9 |
| *Caenis macrura* | 0.018 | 0.236 | 13.12 | 1a |

References: 1, Zelinka, a 1980, b 1973, c 1977; 2, Welton, Ladle & Bass 1982; 3, Brooker & Morris 1978; 4, Obrdlik, Adamek & Zahradka 1979; 5, Zahradka 1978; 6, Tokeshi 1985; 7, Savage 1986; 8, Russev & Doshkinova 1985; 9, Neveu, Lapchin & Vignes 1979.

# LIFE CYCLES

The extensive literature on life cycles of Ephemeroptera has been summarised by Clifford (1982) who includes data on 718 life cycles for 297 species, most of which occur in Europe or North America. He found that about 60% of all life cycles were univoltine (one generation per year), about 30% were multivoltine (more than one generation per year), about 4% were semivoltine (one generation every two, or even three, years) and the remainder were variable. In spite of this wealth of information, little is known about the life cycles of seventeen British species.

Life cycles of most species vary slightly according to environmental conditions but in some species, this variation can be large. For example, *Baetis rhodani* is univoltine in northern Europe above a latitude of 65°N and in mountain areas, bivoltine with both a winter generation and a summer generation throughout most of Europe, and bivoltine with one winter and two summer generations in warmer streams of Southern Europe (see page 102). Therefore the life cycles presented in this section are not the only possible versions that can exist.

It is not always easy to construct life cycles entirely from field data. Laboratory data on larval growth and especially egg hatching are usually essential for the correct interpretation of life cycles in the field. The paucity of such data for many species is a major weakness and further laboratory work may necessitate a re-interpretation of some of the following life cycles.

Whenever possible, the life cycles have been summarised in diagrams that show the months in which eggs (e) and adults (a) occur, and the modal length of the larvae in each month with the length scale simply given as tiny larvae (t), half-grown larvae (h) and full-grown larvae (f). The modal length is the size for the majority of larvae and is often similar to geometric mean length. The flight periods (a) in the diagrams are usually for one locality and are therefore shorter than the general flight periods for many localities (see Table 5 in Elliott & Humpesch 1983).

## *Siphlonuridae*

*Siphlonurus lacustris* is univoltine (fig. 45*a*) with overwintering eggs and larvae (Hynes 1961; Bretschko 1966; Landa 1968; Brittain 1974, 1978, 1980). Adults are usually found in June, July and early August, but have been recorded between May and September (Elliott & Humpesch 1983). In central Europe, this species overwinters only in the egg stage (Landa 1968), and in Norway the larvae are 2-4 mm long when the ice melts in spring but grow rapidly so that adult emergence occurs in August and September (Brittain 1974).

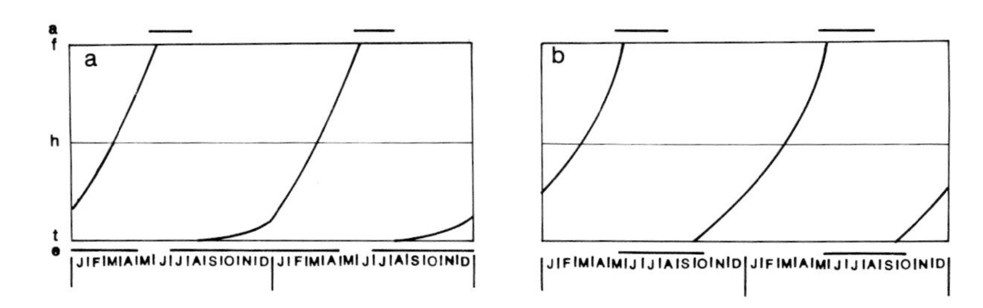


Fig. 45. Siphlonuridae: life cycles of *a*, *Siphlonurus lacustris* (from Hynes 1961); *b*, *Ameletus inopinatus* (from Gledhill 1959) (a, months in which adults occur; f, full-grown larvae; h, half-grown larvae; t, tiny larvae; e, months in which eggs occur).

*Ameletus inopinatus* is also univoltine (fig. 45*b*) with adults present from May to early August (Gledhill 1959; Ulfstrand 1968a; Landa 1968; Brittain 1974, 1978; Sowa 1975c; Andersen, Fjellheim, Larsen & Otto 1978). In Sweden (Ulfstrand 1968a) and Norway (Brittain 1974), the larvae grow under ice and are almost ready to emerge when the ice melts in spring.

Virtually nothing is known about the life cycles of *Siphlonurus armatus* and *S. alternatus*. Adults of both species have been recorded from May to August (Elliott & Humpesch 1983) and both species are probably univoltine. Landa (1968) suggests that both species overwinter in the egg stage.

## *Baetidae*

*Baetis fuscatus* is definitely univoltine, probably bivoltine (fig. 46*a*), with overwintering eggs (Pleskot 1958, 1961; Ulfstrand 1968a; Landa 1968; Langford 1971; Sowa 1975c; Wise 1980). There is very rapid larval growth and there may be more than two generations per year. Pleskot (1961), however, suggested that this multivoltinism may be an artifact due to the successive hatching of egg batches laid in the previous summer. *Baetis scambus* is also bivoltine (fig. 46*b*) with overwintering eggs (Elliott 1967b; Thibault 1971; Fahy 1973; Sowa 1975c, 1979; Armitage 1976; Neveu, Lapchin & Vignes 1979; Wise 1980; Rosillon 1986b). Landa (1968) described this species as univoltine in central Europe. In southern France, larvae are present for a longer period than that shown in fig. 46*b* (Thibault 1971; Neveu, Lapchin & Vignes 1979).

*Baetis vernus* also overwinters in the egg stage (fig. 46*c*) and can be univoltine, bivoltine or multivoltine (Pleskot 1958, 1961; Hynes 1961; Landa 1968; Langford 1971; Illies & Masteller 1977; Sandrock 1978; Andersen, Fjellheim, Larsen & Otto 1978; Sowa 1979; Schmidt 1984).

There is an egg diapause in this species (Bohle 1969); the length of the diapause is largely controlled by temperature and variations in diapause length are probably chiefly responsible for variations in voltinism (Schmidt 1984).

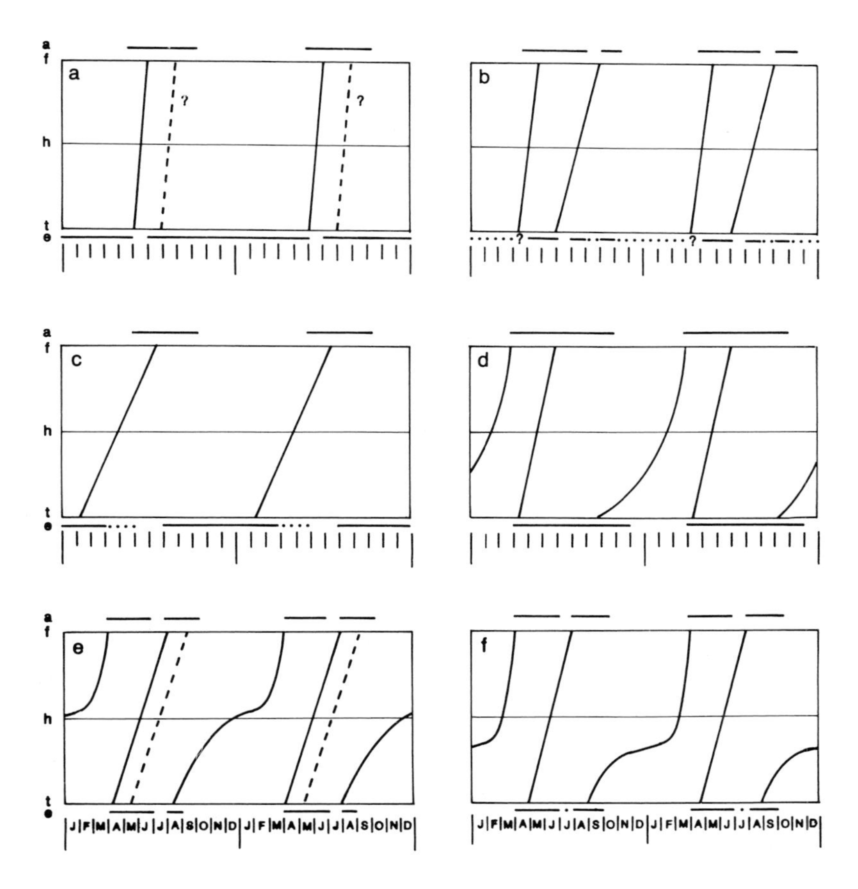


Fig. 46. Baetidae: life cycles of *a*, *Baetis fuscatus* (from Wise 1980); *b*, *Baetis scambus* (from Elliott 1967b; Rosillon 1986b); *c*, *Baetis vernus* (from Bohle 1969; Andersen *et al.* 1978; Schmidt 1984); *d*, *Baetis buceratus* (from Landa 1968; Langford 1971); *e*, *Baetis muticus* (from Macan 1957; Wise 1980); *f*, *Baetis niger* (from Elliott 1967b) (a, months in which adults occur; f, full-grown larvae; h, half-grown larvae; t, tiny larvae; e, months in which eggs occur).

These three species, *B. fuscatus*, *B. scambus*, *B. vernus*, all overwinter in the egg stage and have a variable number of summer generations. Of the other six *Baetis* spp. occurring in the British Isles, virtually nothing is known about *B. digitatus* except that adults have been recorded from May to September (Elliott & Humpesch 1983), and very little is known about *B. atrebatinus* except that the flight period is from May to October (Elliott & Humpesch 1983) and that in central Europe this species is bivoltine with overwintering larvae (Landa 1968). The remaining four species all overwinter in the larval stage. *Baetis buceratus* is bivoltine (fig. 46*d*) with a slow-growing overwintering generation and a fast-growing summer generation; adults can be present from April to October (Landa 1968; Langford 1971; Sowa 1975c). *Baetis muticus* is also bivoltine (fig. 46*e*) with an overwintering generation and a fast-growing summer generation of one or two cohorts; adults can be present from April to October (Macan 1957; Landa 1968; Langford 1971; Sukop 1973; Sowa 1975c, 1979; Andersen, Fjellheim, Larsen & Otto 1978; Wise 1980). In North Sweden, this species overwinters chiefly in the egg stage and is univoltine (Ulfstrand 1968a). In southern France, adults occur from February to December and there are probably three generations (Thibault 1971). *Baetis niger* is also bivoltine (fig. 46*f*) with overwintering and summer generations, adults being present from April to October (Elliott 1967b; Landa 1968; Sowa 1975c).

The last *Baetis* species, *B. rhodani*, is one of the most studied of all Ephemeroptera. It is basically bivoltine (fig. 47*a*) with overwintering and summer generations (Harker 1952; Macan 1957; Pleskot 1958, 1961; Hynes 1961; Elliott 1967b, 1972; Landa 1968; Larsen 1968; Thorup 1963, 1973; Langford 1971; Fahy 1972, 1973; Bengtsson 1973; Sukop 1973; Sowa 1975c, 1979; Sandrock 1978; Brittain 1978, 1979; Humpesch 1979; Mirjana 1979; Wise 1980). This species is univoltine with only the overwintering generation in northern latitudes above 65°N (Ulfstrand 1968a) and in mountainous regions at lower latitudes (Illies 1952; Sowa 1965). There may be an additional summer generation in the warmer streams and rivers of southern Europe (Thibault 1971; Benech 1972b; Neveu, Lapchin & Vignes 1979). Adults of this species usually occur from March to November but have been taken in all months in the British Isles (Elliott & Humpesch 1983). The long flight period, the long period when eggs are present and the multivoltine capacity of the life cycle are the chief reasons why *B. rhodani* is usually the most abundant Ephemeroptera species occurring in running water in the British Isles.

*Centroptilum luteolum* is bivoltine (fig. 47*b*) with a slow-growing overwintering generation and a fast-growing summer generation; adults can be found from April to November (Bretschko 1965; Macan & Maudsley 1968;

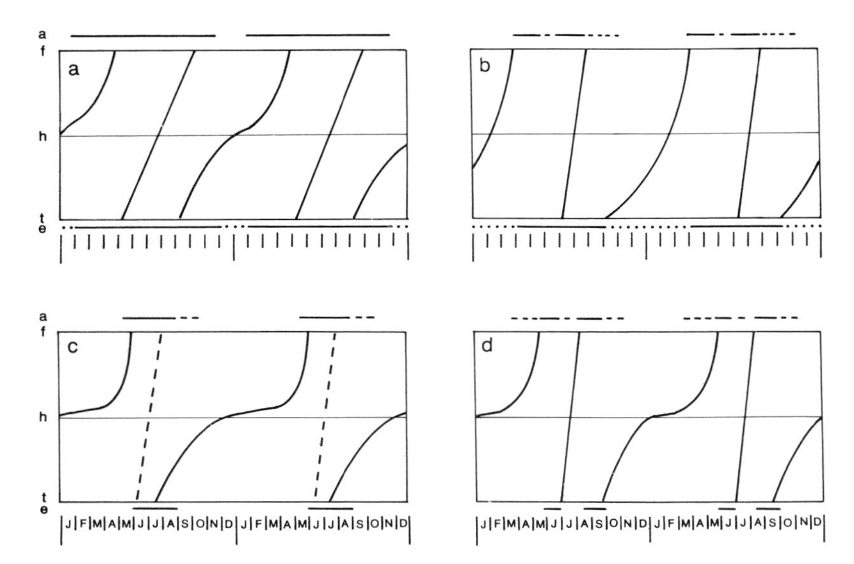


Fig. 47. Baetidae: life cycles of *a, Baetis rhodani* (from Elliott 1967b, 1972); *b, Centroptilum luteolum* (from Wise 1980); *c. Cloeon dipterum* (from Brown 1961b); *d, Cloeon simile* (from Macan 1965) (a, months in which adults occur; f, full-grown larvae; h, half-grown larvae; t, tiny larvae; e, months in which eggs occur).

Lavandier & Dumas 1971; Jazdzewska 1971; Brittain 1974; Sowa 1975c; Macan 1978; Wise 1980). Very little is known about *Centroptilum pennulatum* except that adults have been recorded from May to October (Elliott & Humpesch 1983), and that in central Europe this species overwinters in the egg stage and has more than one generation per year (Landa 1968; Sowa 1975c). A similar life cycle may occur in the River Lune, Northern England, but the data are too sparse for any definite conclusions to be made (Macan 1978).

*Cloeon dipterum* exhibits a wide range of life cycles but always has a slow-growing winter generation (fig. 47*c*) that is often followed by one or more rapidly-growing summer generations so that adults can be found from May to October (Grandi 1941; Schmidt 1951; Brown 1961b; Bretschko 1965; Landa 1968; Crisp & Gledhill 1970; Jazdzewska 1971; Lichtenberg 1973; Kjellberg 1973; Brooker & Edwards 1974; Learner & Potter 1974; Sowa 1975c; Macan 1977; Cianciara 1979, 1980; Nagell 1980, 1981). As this species is ovoviviparous (see page 93), it cannot overwinter in the egg stage but can rapidly produce extra generations in warmer summers. *Cloeon simile* is not ovoviviparous and is usually bivoltine (fig. 47*d*) with winter and summer generations (Macan 1965; Landa 1968; Brittain 1974; Sowa 1975c). In an Austrian pond covered by ice all winter, larvae were not found until the ice had melted, when they grew rapidly to produce one generation (Bretschko 1965). This species has a long flight period, adults can be found from March to November in the British Isles (Elliott & Humpesch 1983). Little is known about *Procloeon bifidum* except that adults have been recorded from April to October (Elliott & Humpesch 1983), and that in central Europe this species has overwintering eggs and more than one generation per year (Landa 1968; Jazdzewska 1971; Sowa 1975c).

*Heptageniidae*

*Rhithrogena semicolorata* is univoltine (fig. 48*a*) with overwintering larvae (Badcock 1949; Harker 1952; Macan 1957; Hynes 1961; Egglishaw & MacKay 1967; Landa 1968; Thibault 1971; Fahy 1973; Sowa 1975c, 1979; Brooker & Morris 1978; Wise 1980). As growth rates vary with water temperature, the periods over which adults emerge also vary from year to year and locality to locality. Adults have been found from April to September in the British Isles (Elliott & Humpesch 1983). As the hatching period for eggs of this species is short (Humpesch & Elliott 1980), it can rarely overwinter in the egg stage. Little is known about *R. germanica* except that adults have been recorded from late March to early May (Elliott & Humpesch 1983) and that the life cycle is probably similar to that of *R. semicolorata* (Landa 1968; Sowa 1975c, 1979; Wise 1980).

*Heptagenia sulphurea* is univoltine (fig. 48*b*) but there is usually a fast-growing cohort that emerges in May/June and a slower-growing cohort that emerges in August/September (Ulfstrand 1968a; Landa 1968; Langford 1971; Langford & Aston 1972; Sowa 1975c, 1979). This species may be also bivoltine with a summer generation in central Europe (Landa 1968). Nothing is known about the life cycle of *H. longicauda* except that adults have been recorded in May and June (Elliott & Humpesch 1983), and very little is known about *H. fuscogrisea* except that it is probably univoltine with overwintering larvae, and adults emerging in May and June (Landa 1968; Bengtsson 1968; Brittain 1974). The fourth British species in this genus, *H. lateralis*, is univoltine (fig. 48*c*) with overwintering larvae (Harker 1952; Jensen 1956; Macan 1957; Hynes 1961; Landa 1968; Sowa 1975c, 1979; Wise 1980). Adults have been found from May to September in the British Isles (Elliott & Humpesch 1983).

Little is known about the life cycle of *Arthroplea congener* but it is probably univoltine with overwintering eggs and rapid larval growth in the summer (Hirvenoja 1964; Landa 1968).

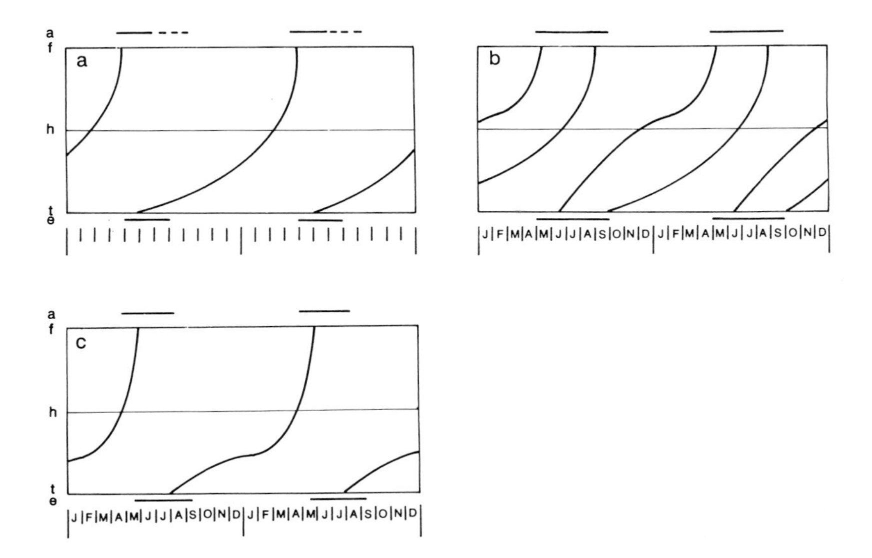


Fig. 48. Heptageniidae: life cycles of *a*, *Rhithrogena semicolorata* (from Wise 1980); *b*, *Heptagenia sulphurea* (from Langford 1971); *c*, *Heptagenia lateralis* (from Macan 1957) (a, months in which adults occur; f, full-grown larvae; h, half-grown larvae; t, tiny larvae; e, months in which eggs occur).

*Ecdyonurus venosus* is univoltine (fig. 49*a*) with overwintering larvae, adults being found from April to July, sometimes to October (Elliott 1967b; Landa 1968; Thibault 1971; Fahy 1973; Sowa 1975c; Wise 1980). Rawlinson (1939), in contrast, concluded that this species was bivoltine with an overwintering generation and a fast-growing summer generation. *Ecdyonurus torrentis* is also univoltine (fig. 49*b*) with an overwintering generation, adults being found from May, sometimes March, to September (Macan 1957, Landa 1968; Sowa 1975c, 1979; Wise 1980). Harker (1952), in contrast, concluded that this species was bivoltine with an overwintering generation of two cohorts and a fast-growing summer generation. *Ecdyonurus dispar* is also univoltine (fig. 49*c*) but there is little retardation in larval growth in winter and adults are found from June to October (Macan & Maudsley 1968; Landa 1968; Sowa 1975c, 1979; Wise 1980). The hatching period for eggs of this species is longer than that for the other three *Ecdyonurus* spp. (Humpesch 1980, and figs 49*a*, *b*, *c*, *d*). *Ecdyonurus insignis* is also univoltine (fig. 49*d*) with overwintering larvae

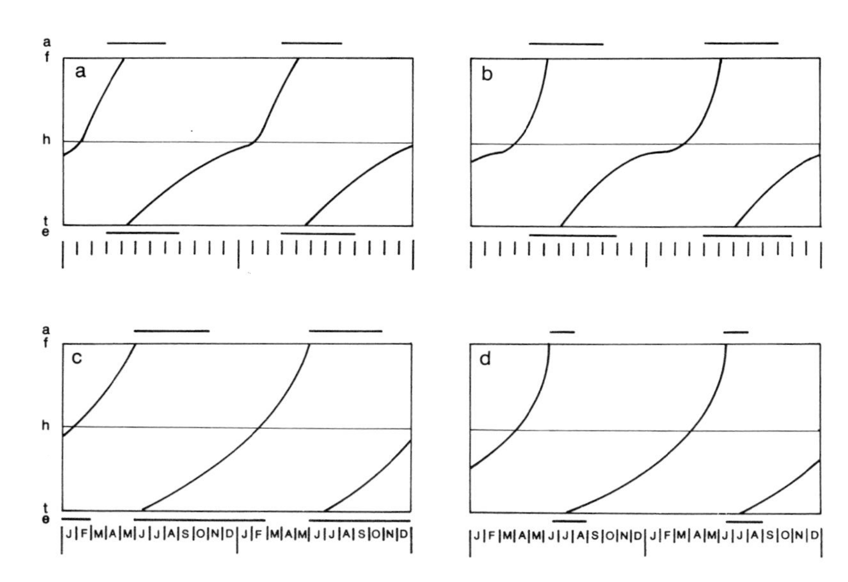


Fig. 49. Heptageniidae: life cycles of *a, Ecdyonurus venosus* (from Elliott 1967b; Humpesch 1980); *b, Ecdyonurus torrentis* (from Macan 1957; Humpesch 1980); *c, Ecdyonurus dispar* (from Macan & Maudsley 1968; Humpesch 1980); *d, Ecdyonurus insignis* (from Humpesch 1980; Macan 1981) (a, months in which adults occur; f, full-grown larvae; h, half-grown larvae; t, tiny larvae; e, months in which eggs occur).

(Macan 1981). In central Europe this species overwinters in the egg stage (Landa 1968; Sowa 1975c, 1979). Although the flight period is short in the example (fig. 49*d*), adults of this species have been found from May to October in the British Isles (Elliott & Humpesch 1983).

### *Leptophlebiidae*

*Leptophlebia marginata* is univoltine (fig. 50*a*) with overwintering larvae (Macan 1965, 1977; Landa 1968; Bengtsson 1968; Brittain 1972, 1974, 1978, 1980; Sowa 1975c, Lingdell & Müller 1979). *Leptophlebia vespertina* is usually univoltine (fig. 50*b*) with overwintering larvae (Macan 1965, 1977; Landa 1968; Ulfstrand 1969; Brittain 1972, 1974, 1976, 1978, 1980; Kjellberg 1972, 1973; Sowa 1975c; Savage 1986). In the mountains of Sweden, *L. vespertina* is semivoltine (Kjellberg 1973). The two *Leptophlebia* spp. have similar life cycles but adults of *L. marginata* always emerge earlier than those of *L. vespertina*. The latter species has the longest flight period, adults being found from April to August, in contrast with April

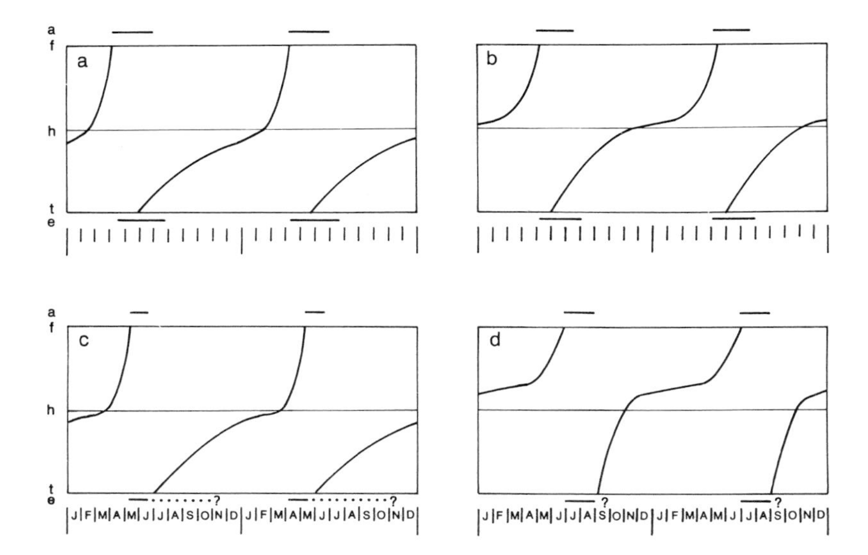


Fig. 50. Leptophlebiidae: life cycles of *a*, *Leptophlebia marginata* (from Macan 1965); *b*, *Leptophlebia vespertina* (from Brittain 1976; Savage 1986); *c*, *Paraleptophlebia submarginata* (from Macan 1957; Fahy 1973); *d*, *Habrophlebia fusca* (from Landa 1968) (a, months in which adults occur; f, full-grown larvae; h, half-grown larvae; t, tiny larvae; e, months in which eggs occur).

to June for *L. marginata* (Elliott & Humpesch 1983).

*Paraleptophlebia submarginata* is univoltine (fig. 50*c*) with overwintering larvae (Macan 1957; Landa 1968; Thibault 1971; Lavandier & Dumas 1971; Fahy 1973; Sowa 1975c; Wise 1980). Adults have been taken from April to July in the British Isles (Elliott & Humpesch 1983) but a longer flight period from March to November has been recorded in southern France (Lavandier & Dumas 1971). Little is known about the life cycles of *P. cincta* and *P. werneri* except that adults have been found from May to August and May to June respectively in the British Isles (Elliott & Humpesch 1983). According to Landa (1968), both species overwinter in the egg stage and have fast-growing summer generations, but Sowa (1975c) found that *P. cincta* overwinters in the larval stage.

Little is known about the life cycle of *Habrophlebia fusca* except that adults have been found from May to September in the British Isles (Elliott & Humpesch 1983), and that it is univoltine with overwintering larvae (fig. 50*d*) in central Europe (Landa 1957, 1968).

*Potamanthidae*

Little is known about the life cycle of *Potamanthus luteus* except that adults have been found from May to July in the British Isles (Elliott & Humpesch 1983), and that it is univoltine in central Europe with rapid growth in autumn so that it overwinters as large larvae (Landa 1968; Sowa 1975c).

*Ephemeridae*

Little is known about the life cycle of *Ephemera vulgata* in the British Isles except that adults occur from May to August (Elliott & Humpesch 1983). This species is semivoltine in Sweden (fig. 51*a*) with little growth in winter (Kjellberg 1973). *Ephemera danica* is usually semivoltine (fig. 51*b*) but some populations have been reported as univoltine, or mixed univoltine/semivoltine, or having a life cycle lasting three years (Illies 1952; Pleskot 1958, 1961; Landa 1968; Thibault 1971; Jazdzewska 1971; Svensson 1976, 1977; Sowa 1975c, 1979; Whelan 1980; Otto & Svensson 1981; Wright, Hiley & Berrie 1981; Tokeshi 1985). Tokeshi (1985) estimated the number of degree-days required to complete larval growth and then used temperature data from other sites in Europe to predict the length of the larval growth period. As the predicted values were similar to the published accounts of the length of the life cycle, it would appear that differences in temperature regimes could explain the varying length of the life cycle for different populations. Little is known about the life cycle of *Ephemera lineata* except that adults have been caught in July in the British Isles (Elliott & Humpesch 1983), and that this species is semivoltine in central Europe (Landa 1968; Sowa 1975c).

*Ephemerellidae*

Many workers have found that *Ephemerella ignita* is univoltine (fig. 51*c*) with overwintering eggs (e.g. Illies 1952; Macan 1957; Pleskot 1958, 1961; Hynes 1961; Maitland 1965; Elliott 1967b; Landa 1968; Arnold & Macan 1969; Langford 1971; Sowa 1975c; Armitage 1976; Brooker & Morris 1978; Wise 1980; Jazdzewska 1980; Rosillon 1986b). In several of these studies, small larvae were found in October and November, long after the flight period, but it was concluded that these larvae did not survive the winter (Pleskot 1958; Hynes 1961; Elliott 1967b; Wise 1980; Rosillon 1986b). However, in warmer streams of southern Ireland, England and France, larvae are present throughout the year, including the winter, and there may be both winter and summer generations (Langford & Bray 1969;

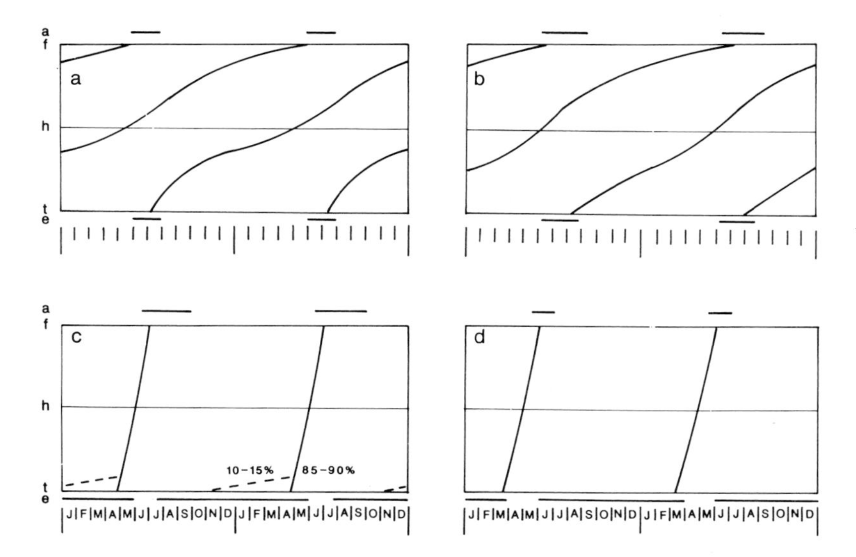


Fig. 51. Ephemeridae: life cycles of *a, Ephemera vulgata* (from Kjellberg 1973); *b, Ephemera danica* (from Tokeshi 1985). Ephemerellidae: life cycles of *c, Ephemerella ignita* (from Elliott 1967b, 1978); *d, Ephemerella notata* (from Wise 1980) (a, months in which adults occur; f, full-grown larvae; h, half-grown larvae; t, tiny larvae; e, months in which eggs occur).

Thibault 1971; Lavandier & Dumas 1971; Fahy 1973; Bass 1976; Neveu, Lapchin & Vignes 1979). These differences can be explained by the results of a detailed study on egg hatching in this species (Elliott 1978). In a small, cool stream in the English Lake District, 10-15% of the eggs hatched between October and late February, and the rest hatched in March, April and May (fig. 51*c*). It was also shown that if water temperatures had been higher, then more eggs would have hatched in the autumn as obviously occurs in warmer streams. *Ephemerella notata* is also univoltine and overwinters either in the egg stage (fig. 51*d* and Wise 1980), or in the egg and larval stages (Hynes 1961), or as tiny larvae (Landa 1968; Sowa 1975c). In all three cases, larval growth is rapid at the end of the winter so that adult emergence occurs in spring, usually just before that of *E. ignita*, Adults of *E. notata* have been found only in May and June in the British Isles, whereas adults of *E. ignita* can be taken from April to September (Elliott & Humpesch 1983).

*Caenidae*

Little is known about the life cycle of *Brachycercus harrisella* except that adults have been caught in July in the British Isles (Elliott & Humpesch 1983), and that this species is univoltine with overwintering eggs in central Europe (Landa 1968; Sowa 1975c). The small amount of information on the life cycle of *Caenis macrura* suggests that this species is probably bivoltine with overwintering larvae (Landa 1968; Thibault 1971; Sowa 1975c; Mackey 1978). Adults have been found from May to August in the British Isles (Elliott & Humpesch 1983).

*Caenis luctuosa* can be univoltine (Brittain 1974) or bivoltine (fig. 52*a*; Landa 1968; Mol 1983), but always overwinters in the larval stage. Adults have been found from June to September in the British Isles (Elliott & Humpesch 1983). *Caenis robusta* can also be univoltine (fig. 52*b*; Bradbeer & Savage 1980) or bivoltine (Landa 1968), but always overwinters in the larval stage. Adults occur in June and July in the British Isles (Elliott & Humpesch 1983). *Caenis horaria* can be bivoltine (Landa 1968) but is usually univoltine (fig. 52*c*) with overwintering larvae (Mocn 1938;

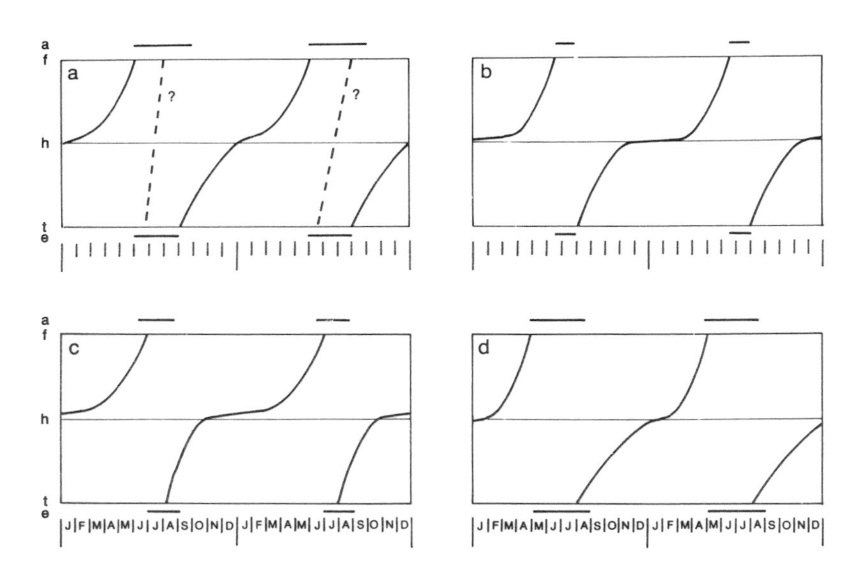


Fig. 52. Caenidae: life cycles of *a*, *Caenis luctuosa* (from Mol 1983); *b*, *Caenis robusta* (from Bradbeer & Savage 1980); *c*, *Caenis horaria* (from Moon 1938); *d*, *Caenis rivulorum* (from Fahy 1973) (a, months in which adults occur; f, full-grown larvae; h, half-grown larvae; t, tiny larvae; e, months in which eggs occur).

Jazdzewska 1971; Lichtenberg 1973; Brittain 1974). Adults have been found from May to September in the British Isles (Elliott & Humpesch 1983) and a similar long flight period has been reported from Finland (Aro 1928). *Caenis rivulorum* is univoltine (fig. 52*d*) with overwintering larvae (Thibault 1971; Fahy 1973; Sowa 1975c; Armitage 1976; Neveu, Lapchin & Vignes 1979). Adults have been found from May to September in the British Isles (Elliott & Humpesch 1983). Little is known about the life cycle of *Caenis pusilla* but it is probably univoltine with overwintering larvae (Malzacher 1986).

### *General summary of life cycles*

The British species can be classified into five categories according to whether they are univoltine, bivoltine/multivoltine, or semivoltine, and whether they overwinter in the egg or larval stage. Some species occur in more than one category (indicated by 'part' in parenthesis). In the following list, a question mark indicates that little is known about the life cycle and the classification is simply a guess, usually based on work in central Europe.

GROUP 1A. Univoltine (one generation per year), overwinter in egg stage.

*Siphlonurus lacustris* (part), *S. armatus* (?), *S. alternatus* (?), *Baetis fuscatus* (part), *B. vernus* (part), *Arthroplea congener* (?), *Paraleptophlebia cincta* (? part), *P. werneri* (?), *Ephemerella ignita* (part), *E. notata* (part), *Brachycercus harrisella* (?).

GROUP 1B. Univoltine, overwinter in larval stage.

*Siphlonurus lacustris* (part), *Ameletus inopinatus*, *Rhithrogena semicolorata*, *R. germanica* (?), *Heptagenia sulphurea*, *H. fuscogrisea* (?), *H. lateralis*, *Ecdyonurus venosus*, *E. torrentis*, *E. dispar*, *E. insignis*, *Leptophlebia marginata*, *L. vespertina*, *Paraleptophlebia submarginata*, *P. cincta* (? part), *Habrophlebia fusca*, *Potamanthus luteus* (?). *Ephemera danica* (part), *Ephemerella ignita* (part), *E. notata* (part), *Caenis luctuosa* (part), *C. robusta* (part), *C. horaria* (part), *C. rivulorum*, *C. pusilla* (?).

GROUP 2A. Bivoltine (two generations per year) or multivoltine (more than two generations per year), overwinter in egg stage.

*Baetis fuscatus* (part), *B. scambus*, *B. vernus* (part), *Centroptilum pennulatum* (?), *Procloeon bifidum* (?).

GROUP 2B. Bivoltine or multivoltine, overwinter in larval stage.

*Baetis atrebatinus* (?), *B. buceratus*, *B. muticus*, *B. niger*, *B. rhodani*, *Centroptilum luteolum*, *Cloeon dipterum*, *C. simile*, *Ephemerella ignita* (part), *Caenis macrura* (?), *C. luctuosa* (part), *C. robusta* (part), *C. horaria* (part).

GROUP 3. Semivoltine (one generation every two years or even every three years).

*Ephemera vulgata*, *E. danica* (part), *E. lineata* (?)

[NOTHING KNOWN: *Baetis digitatus*, *Heptagenia longicauda*]

The commonest type of life cycle is clearly univoltine with overwintering larvae, followed by bivoltine/multivoltine with overwintering larvae and univoltine with overwintering eggs. Few species are bivoltine/multivoltine with overwintering eggs and the *Ephemera* spp. are the only British species with life cycles taking longer than one year. The large number of question marks indicates that little is known about the life cycles of seventeen British species and clearly more work is required in this field.

## MOVEMENTS OF LARVAE

The term 'invertebrate drift' describes the downstream movement in the water column of benthic invertebrates that usually live on or amongst the substratum of streams and rivers. Although there are a few earlier records (e.g. Needham 1928; Mottram 1932; and references in Elliott 1967a), most information on invertebrate drift has appeared in the last 25 years. Interest greatly increased when it was shown independently in several countries that the downstream movement followed a diel rhythmic pattern: Japan (Tanaka 1960), U.S.A. (Waters 1962), Germany (Müller 1963a, b, c, 1966), Sweden (Sodergren 1963), British Isles (Elliott 1965a, 1967a, b), Norway (Elliott 1965b) and Eastern U.S.S.R (Levanidova & Levanidov 1965). Larvae of Ephemeroptera were a major component of the drift in all these pioneer studies with a total of thirty species being recorded (see species list in Elliott 1967b).

This early work stimulated many investigations on the mechanisms responsible for invertebrate drift, on the role of drift as a dispersal mechanism and on the importance of drift as a food for fish, especially salmonids. There are now over 400 publications in this field and several excellent reviews (Waters 1972; Bournaud & Thibault 1973; Müller 1974,

1982; Adamus & Gaufin 1976; Williams 1981; Wiley & Kohler 1984; Statzner, Dejoux & Elouard 1984). Because of limitations of space, the following account has to be brief with emphasis on aspects relevant to Ephemeroptera.

There is clear nocturnal periodicity in the downstream drifting of Ephemeroptera larvae but the nocturnal peaks may occur at different times for the same species or for closely-related species, e.g. work on *Baetis* spp. (Waters 1962; Müller 1963a, 1966; Elliott 1967a, 1968; Elliott & Minshall 1968). One possible reason for this discrepancy is that different workers have used different sampling periods. As the length of the sampling period increases, the number of detectable peaks decreases (fig. 53; Elliott 1969, 1970a). Although this nocturnal periodicity is typical of larval Ephemeroptera, at high altitudes the drift activity may become desynchronized in continuous daylight (Müller 1970, 1973).

As total discharge is one of the chief factors affecting the magnitude of invertebrate drift, it is preferable to use drift density (number per unit volume of water) rather than drift rate (number of invertebrates passing a sampling point in unit time, usually a day) in the assessment of other causative factors (see review of methodology by Elliott 1970a). Drift density of larval Ephemeroptera can be affected by many factors including their density in the benthos (Waters 1961; Dimond 1967; Pearson & Franklin 1968; Gyselman 1980; but see also contradictory evidence in Elliott 1967a, b; Elliott & Minshall 1968; Hildebrand 1974; Neveu & Echaubard 1975; Bohle 1978; Corkum 1978; Ciborowski 1983), temperature changes (Müller 1966; Wojtalik & Walters 1970; Keller 1975), oxygen concentration (Lavandier & Capblancq 1975; Wiley & Kohler 1980), the water velocity to which the larvae are exposed (Butz 1979; Ciborowski, Pointing & Corkum 1977; Corkum, Pointing & Ciborowski 1977; Ciborowski 1983), larval morphology (Ciborowski & Corkum 1980), larval growth rates (Waters 1966; Müller 1966, 1970; Elliott 1967b; Steine 1972; Keller 1975; Hall, Waters & Cook 1980), food availability (Elliott 1967a, 1968; Bishop & Hynes 1969a; Hildebrand 1974; Keller 1975; Bohle 1978; Kohler 1985) and escape from predatory invertebrates, especially larval Plecoptera (Keller 1975; Corkum & Pointing 1979; Peckarsky 1980; Corkum & Clifford 1980; Walton 1980). As many of these factors interact, it is not surprising that an integrated, predictive model for drift has yet to be produced.

It is even more difficult to explain the nocturnal periodicity in the drifting of larval Ephemeroptera. When this periodicity was first discovered, it was soon shown in field and laboratory experiments that the drifting occurred chiefly at low levels of light intensity, the threshold for the start of drift activity being about 1-30 lux at the water surface, that continuous

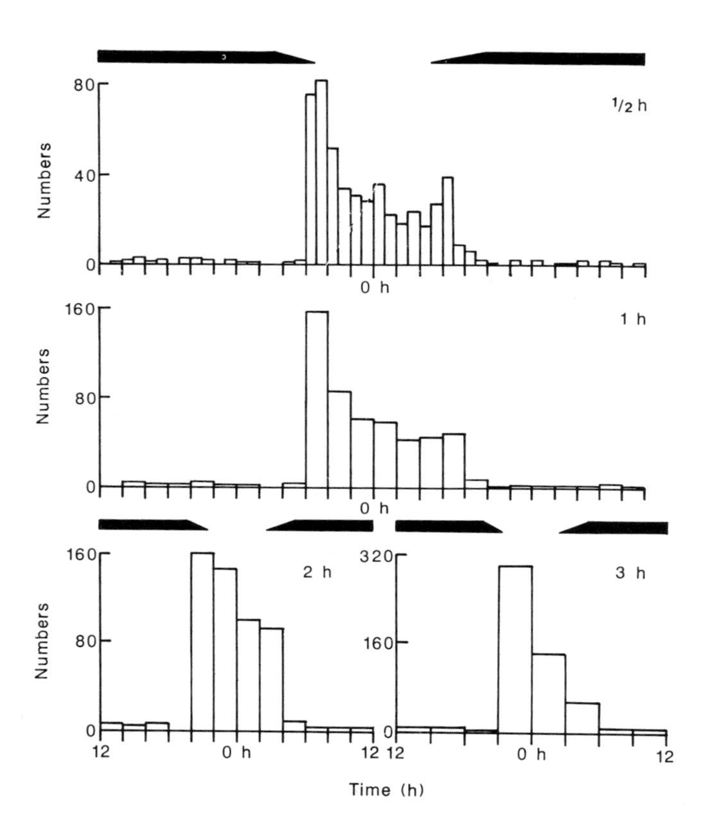


Fig. 53. The diel drift pattern of larvae of *Baetis rhodani* in July. Ordinate: number of larvae taken in a drift sample over a period of $\frac{1}{2}$ h, 1 h, 2 h or 3 h. Abscissa: time in hours with 0 h indicating midnight (shaded portion at the top of each figure indicates the night period). The original samples, taken over periods of $\frac{1}{2}$ h, showed peaks at dusk and dawn with minor peaks during the night. When adjacent samples were combined for the larger periods of 1-3 h, there was a reduction in the number of peaks with only the dusk peak remaining throughout (data from Elliott 1969).

light suppressed the nocturnal drift, and that continuous dark did not suppress drifting but did gradually eliminate the rhythmic periodicity (Elliott 1965a, 1967a; Müller 1965, 1966; Holt & Waters 1967; Bishop 1969; Chaston 1969; Haney *et al.* 1983).

The percentage of the bottom fauna that is drifting in the water column above a unit area of bottom at any instant in time is very low, usually 0·01-0·5% (Elliott 1965b, 1967a, 1971b; Ulfstrand 1968b; Bishop & Hynes 1969a; Radford & Hartland-Rowe 1971; Neveu & Echaubard 1975; Hemsworth & Brooker 1979; Williams 1980). This low percentage was one of the chief reasons for the hypothesis proposed by Elliott (1967a): that the number of detached invertebrates in the drift reflects both the number of invertebrates moving over the exposed parts of stones and plants, and the extent of the competition between these invertebrates for food and space. Therefore, as the activity of most stream invertebrates increases at night when they forage for food, the drift density also increases and there is a nocturnal periodicity in the diel pattern of drift. Although this hypothesis implies that entry into the drift is essentially passive, being due to accidental dislodgement, it does not exclude the possibility that entry can also be active especially when resources, such as food and space, are limited.

Soon after this hypothesis was proposed, a laboratory study of diel activity patterns of five species (*Baetis rhodani*, *Ephemerella ignita*, *Ecdyonurus venosus*, *Rhithrogena semicolorata*, *Heptagenia lateralis*) showed that although the larvae were more active on the substratum at night, the diel pattern of activity did not correspond with that shown by the same species in the drift (Elliott 1968). Similar results were obtained for an Australian species (Bailey 1981). Both studies showed that more larvae were on the upper surfaces of stones by night than by day, and this would obviously increase the probability of a larva entering the drift. Other workers, however, have found no similar movement onto the upper surfaces of stones and have concluded that there is no correlation between drift and activity on the substratum (Bohle 1978; Kohler 1983; Statzner & Mogel 1985; Allan, Flecker & McClintock 1986). In contrast, drift rate was exponentially related to activity for a North American *Baetis* sp. (Ploskey & Brown 1980). These discrepancies may be due to differences in food availability in the different studies. There is some evidence that drifting increases when food patches are sparse and the larvae abandon substrata by entering the water column (Bohle 1978; Kohler 1985). One advantage of drifting at night is that it reduces the probability of being eaten by fish (Allan 1978, 1984).

Although this brief review has emphasized behavioural aspects of invertebrate drift, drifting can also be an escape mechanism from unfavourable conditions. For example, although drift rate usually decreases with decreasing discharge, it may increase when stream discharge is reduced to very low levels (Elliott 1967a; Minshall & Winger 1968; Waters 1969; Corrarino & Brusven 1983). Drift rates may also increase in response to pollutants, including thermal discharges (Coutant 1964; Besch 1966;

Wojtalik & Waters 1970; Decamps & Elliott 1972; Larimore 1974; Brusven & MacPhee 1974; Wallace & Hynes 1975; Crowther & Hynes 1977; Dejoux & Elouard 1977; Muirhead-Thomson 1978; Hall, Pratt & Likens 1982; Allard & Moreau 1984; Bournaud, Maucet & Chavanon 1984; Leland 1985; Swain & White 1985). The extensive literature on the effects of pesticides on drift rates has recently been reviewed by Muirhead-Thomson (1987).

Whatever its cause, the downstream drifting of eggs and larvae could lead to depopulation of upstream areas of streams and rivers. Müller (1954) proposed that there was a compensatory upstream flight of adults, especially females about to lay their eggs. He used the term 'colonisation-cycle' to describe the whole process of eggs and larvae drifting downstream and adults flying upstream, and has recently reviewed work supporting his hypothesis (Müller 1982). Several workers have demonstrated upstream flight in adult Ephemeroptera (Russev 1959, 1973; Thomas 1975; Madsen, Bengtsson & Butz 1973, 1977; Lingdell & Müller 1979; Engblom, Lingdell & Müller 1981; Lavandier 1982). Others have concluded that such movements occur only over short distances and that the direction of flight is determined largely by the wind (Elliott 1967a; Waters 1969; Bishop & Hynes 1969a; Keller 1975; Gyselman 1980), or that an upstream movement occurs in some species but not in other species of Ephemeroptera in the same stream (Bird & Hynes 1981a)

The upstream flight of the adults is not the only possible compensatory mechanism for invertebrate drift; the aquatic stages of many species also move upstream on and amongst the substratum (see review by Söderström 1987). Spectacular upstream movements of large numbers of larval Ephemeroptera have been recorded for the North American species, *Leptophlebia cupida* (Neave 1930; Hayden & Clifford 1974) and the European species, *Parameletus chelifer* (Olsson & Söderström 1978), when they move from the main river into tributaries or areas flooded by spring snow-melt. The latter species appeared to show a 'reversed-colonisation-cycle' with an upstream movement of larvae and a subsequent downstream return flight of adults.

Less spectacular upstream movements on or amongst the substratum have been recorded for many stream invertebrates, including several species of Ephemeroptera (Harker 1953; Verrier 1953; Hultin, Svensson & Ulfstrand 1969; Bishop & Hynes 1969b; Elliott 1971a; Keller 1975; Bird & Hynes 1981b; McArthur & Barnes 1985). More larvae move upstream at night than during the day and a definite diel periodicity in upstream movement has been shown in *Baetis rhodani* (Elliott 1971a). Most larvae move upstream amongst the small stones and gravel near the banks but large larvae of *B. rhodani* can move upstream in midstream. These upstream movements only partially compensate for downstream drift; the number of invertebrates moving upstream per day being 2-39% of the number drifting downstream (Bishop & Hynes 1969b; Elliott 1971a; Bird & Hynes 1981b). The distances travelled upstream on or amongst the substratum were similar for six Ephemeroptera species in a Lake District stream; ranges for marked larvae in the stream and unmarked larvae in experimental channels in the stream were 0-6 m for *Ecdyonurus torrentis*, 1-5 m for *E. venosus*, 0-6 m for *Heptagenia lateralis*, 0-6 m for *Rhithrogena semicolorata*, 3·25 m for *Ephemerella ignita*, 3-5 m for *Baetis rhodani* (Elliott 1971a).

Although at first, it appears logical to assume that there must be a need for some kind of upstream movement to compensate for downstream drifting, such a compensatory movement may not be necessary for species that drift only short distances before returning to the bottom. Several workers have concluded that most drifting invertebrates travel only 1-10 m before returning to the stream bed (Elliott 1967a, 1971b; McLay 1970; Townsend & Hildrew 1976; Ciborowski & Corkum 1980; Campbell 1985; Larkin & McKone 1985; Otto & Sjöstrom 1986). Some workers (Waters 1965; McLay 1970) have tended to over-emphasize the maximum distance travelled, but from McLay's own results showing a maximum distance of 46·7 m, it can be shown that 60% of invertebrates caught in his drift net were derived from within 10 m upstream and more than 40% from within 6 m.

The mean distances travelled by drifting invertebrates in experiments in a Lake District stream were affected by water velocity and the type of substratum, but not by the source of the experimental animals (benthos or drift), by changes in illumination (daylight or darkness), or by seasonal changes, including water temperature (Elliott 1971b). Ranges for mean distances travelled were 1·8-17·5 m for *Rhithrogena semicolorata*, 1·6-10·6 m for *Ecdyonurus venosus*, 3·5-5·8 m for *Ephemerella ignita* and 1·0-5·6 m for *Baetis rhodani*, all on a stony substratum, but only 1·0-2·1 m for *E. ignita* and 1·0-2·0 m for *B. rhodani* on a substratum with dense stands of macrophytes (chiefly *Callitriche aquatica*). These species are therefore well adapted to return rapidly to the bottom and short excursions into the drift are probably part of their normal behavioural activity.

As well as downstream drifting and upstream movements, there are also vertical movements amongst the substratum, especially in response to spates (Clifford 1966; Williams & Hynes 1974; Poole & Steward 1976), and lateral movements, usually towards the banks (Verrier 1956; Elliott 1971a; Williams 1981; Williams & Hynes 1976). The latter movements are most pronounced just prior to adult emergence in species that moult to the subimago after the larvae have left the water, e.g. *Leptophlebia* spp.,

*Siphlonurus* spp. (Elliott & Humpesch 1983).

There are therefore four types of movement for Ephemeroptera in running water (fig. 54): downstream (in the water column as drift and on/amongst the substratum), upstream (as adults, especially ovipositing females, and as larvae on/amongst the substratum), vertical (amongst the substratum), lateral (on/amongst the substratum). Many species move in all four directions at different times in their life cycle and these movements are an important part of the dynamics of Ephemeroptera populations.

Although movements of benthic invertebrates have been studied largely in running water, similar movements probably occur in lakes but the evidence is sparse. Some Ephemeroptera species move towards the shore prior to emergence, e.g. *Leptophlebia* spp. (Macan 1965; Macan & Maudsley 1968; Savage 1986). Larval Ephemeroptera have also been caught in traps or tow nets, sometimes well above the lake bed, and night catches usually exceed day catches (Moon 1940; Mundie 1959; Pieczynski 1964; Solem 1973; Macan & Kitching 1976; Andrikovics 1981). There is clearly a need for more information on the activity patterns and movements of Ephemeroptera in lakes.

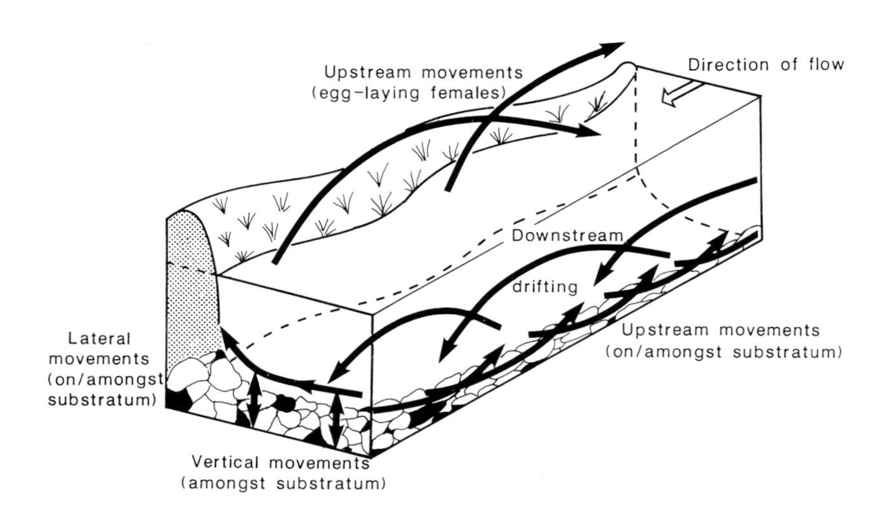


Fig. 54. Summary diagram of movements of Ephemeroptera in running water.

# APPLIED ASPECTS OF EPHEMEROPTERA ECOLOGY

The earliest recorded observations on Ephemeroptera were probably made by the Greek philosopher Aristotle (384-322 B.C.) who described the chief features of the life cycle. Although other early descriptions followed, they added little to Aristotle's original account. The first detailed description of the life cycle of a species was by Outgert Cluyt in 1634 followed by a more famous account by Jan Swammerdam in 1675 (Francissen & Mol 1984; Mol 1984). Both studies were made in the Netherlands and the subject is now called *Palingenia longicauda*. It is sad that this species is now extinct in western Europe, including the Netherlands (Illies 1978; Russev 1987).

As many species of Ephemeroptera occurring in running water are sensitive to various forms of pollution, their presence and diversity can be used to indicate water quality. The 'Saprobic system' of water quality is an empirical system based on different levels of organic enrichment. In the version by Sladecek (1973), twenty-two of the forty-eight British species are listed as indicators of saprobity (Table 11). Ten species indicate zeno- and oligo-saprobity (zones without organic enrichment), twelve species indicate beta-mesosaprobity (zones with minor organic enrichment), and none indicates alpha-mesosaprobity or polysaprobity (zones with major organic enrichment). Ephemeroptera larvae are used for other indices of water quality, but the only named species is *Baetis rhodani*, e.g. Trent biotic index, Chandler biotic score, Biological Monitoring Working Party Score (see reviews by Hellawell 1978, 1986).

The latter reviews also summarise the advantages of using benthic macroinvertebrates, including Ephemeroptera, for routine surveillance of water quality. Chemical analyses can provide valuable information on water quality but, unless the chemical monitoring is continuous, it is easy to miss a sudden, short change in water quality. The most useful, and probably cheapest, continuous recorders are therefore the living organisms, especially those that are sensitive to changes in water quality. The level of change that can be detected will depend upon the type of organism, the level of identification, the sampling strategy, the data analysis and the natural variation in the composition, numbers and biomass of the organisms used (Elliott, Drake & Tullett 1980). The advantages of Ephemeroptera are that they can be identified to species, they are relatively easy to sample, and most species are present throughout the year.

TABLE 11. EPHEMEROPTERA SPECIES USED AS INDICATORS OF SAPROBITY (FROM SLADEČEK 1973)

x = xeno-saprobity, o = oligo-saprobity, $\beta$ = beta-mesosaprobity, $\alpha$ = alpha-mesosaprobity, p = polysaprobity.

| | x | x-o | o | o-$\beta$ | $\beta$ | ($\beta$-$\alpha$) ($\alpha$) | ($\alpha$-p) (p) |
|---|---|---|---|---|---|---|---|
| *Ameletus inopinatus* | + | | | | | | |
| *Baetis fuscatus* | | | | | + | | |
| *B. scambus* | | | | + | | | |
| *B. rhodani* | | + | | | | | |
| *B. muticus* | | | | + | | | |
| *B. vernus* | | | | | + | | |
| *Centroptilum luteolum* | | | | | + | | |
| *Cloeon dipterum* | | | | | + | | |
| *Rhithrogena semicolorata* | + | | | | | | |
| *Heptagenia sulphurea* | | | | | + | | |
| *H. fuscogrisea* | | | | | + | | |
| *H. lateralis* | | | | | + | | |
| *Ecdyonurus venosus* | | | + | | | | |
| *E. dispar* | | | | | + | | |
| *E. insignis* | | | | | + | | |
| *Paraleptophlebia submarginata* | | | | + | | | |
| *Habrophlebia fusca* | | | | + | | | |
| *Potamanthus luteus* | | | | | + | | |
| *Ephemera vulgata* | | | | | + | | |
| *E. danica* | | | | + | | | |
| *Ephemerella ignita* | | | | | + | | |
| *Caenis macrura* | | + | | | | | |

In recent years, acidification of surface waters has become a major issue and Ephemeroptera larvae are among the most sensitive of aquatic insects. As acidification increases, Ephemeroptera species progressively disappear until none remains, even though other groups of aquatic insects are still flourishing (e.g. Sutcliffe & Carrick 1973; Leivestad *et al.* 1976; Nilssen 1980; Harriman & Morrison 1982). In a survey of 600, otherwise unpolluted, streams in Sweden, the number of Ephemeroptera species was highest in the pH range 6·0-7·5, much lower in the range 5·0-6·0, reduced to only three in the range 4·0-5·0 (*Leptophlebia vespertina*, *L. marginata*, *Heptagenia fuscogrisea*) and reduced to only *L. vespertina* at a pH $<$4·0 (Johansson & Nyberg 1981). Other species of Ephemeroptera have been found at low pH. For example, *Baetis rhodani* was recorded in Swedish streams at pH 4·5 (Engblom & Lingdell 1984) and *B. rhodani* and other *Baetis* spp. occurred at mean pH 4·7 and 4·45 in two streams in the English Peak District (Aston *et al.* 1985). It is possible that the adverse effects of high acidity were reduced by relatively higher concentrations of calcium, alkalinity, sodium, potassium and chloride.

Although Ephemeroptera are often sensitive to pollution, the IUCN invertebrate red data book lists only one species that is at risk, the Australian *Tasmanophlebia lacus-coerulei* (Wells, Pyle & Collins 1983). Several species in central Europe have been reported as endangered or extinct (Blab *et al.* 1984). The latter group includes the historically famous *Palingenia longicauda*. Sadly, the spectacular mass emergence of this species in the Bulgarian section of the River Danube (Russev 1973, 1987) can now be seen only in photographs. The status of some of the British species is uncertain. There is only one doubtful record for *Arthroplea congener* (Blair 1929) and this species may not occur in the British Isles. *Heptagenia longicauda* once occurred in southern England but may now be extinct (Macan 1958). *Potamanthus luteus* and *Ephemera lineata* are very rare species that appear to be restricted to large rivers such as the Thames, Usk and Wye (Harrisson 1958; Edwards & Brooker 1982).

Larval Ephemeroptera contribute up to 25% of the total zoobenthos production in cooler, unpolluted streams and rivers. They are therefore an important source of food for fish, especially salmonids, e.g. brown trout and sea-trout (*Salmo trutta* L.), young salmon (*S. salar* L.) and rainbow trout (*S. gairdneri* Richardson). Invertebrate drift is an important food source for salmonids, especially the young fish, and several studies have shown that larvae, subimagines and imagines of Ephemeroptera are an important component of this drift food (e.g. Elliott 1967c, 1970b, 1973; Jenkins, Feldmeth & Elliott 1970; Metz 1974; Allan 1978, 1981, 1983; Bisson 1978). It is therefore not surprising that imitations of Ephemeroptera have been used by fishermen for several centuries, especially in pursuit of fish of the salmonid family. Imitations of larvae and emerging subimagines are used as 'wet-flies' below the water surface, and imitations of emerged subimagines and imagines are used as 'dry-flies' on the water surface. Each type of fly has a common name as well as a latin name but, unfortunately, many species have more than one common name and the same common name is sometimes used for more than one species (see review by Elliott & Humpesch 1983).

As well as fish, there are other vertebrates that feed on aquatic insects, including Ephemeroptera. For example, the dipper (*Cinclus cinclus* (L.)) specialises in the capture of stream insects and can swim under water (Ormerod 1985). In a survey of breeding dippers at 74 sites on Welsh streams, the birds were absent from sites with lower pH and a paucity of food organisms, including Ephemeroptera; increasing acidification could therefore be detrimental to populations of dippers by reducing their food supply (Ormerod *et al.* 1986).

Ephemeroptera have therefore been used by man for many centuries. First as a bait for fish and then replaced by more robust imitations made of fur, feathers and wool. More recently, they have been used as indicators of water quality and have been shown to be an essential component of many aquatic communities, providing food not only for fish but also for a variety of birds and mammals. It is less easy to quantify their aesthetic value but many ecologists have derived pleasure from their contact with Ephemeroptera, not only because of their elegance of adaptation but also because of their inherent beauty. Modern scientific writers, particularly in professional journals, are discouraged from expressing such feelings on the grounds that they introduce unnecessary words. However, the appreciation of beauty is often apparent in illustrations such as those drawn by Professor Marie Mizzaro-Wimmer in this book.

# ACKNOWLEDGEMENTS

We wish to thank Mrs P. A. Tullett for all her assistance in the preparation of this booklet, T. Gledhill and T. I. Furnass for their assistance with the preparation of the illustrations, Dr P. Malzacher, Dr C. M. Drake, Dr T. Soldan and D. Hefti for supplying specimens, Mrs J. Hawksford for typing the manuscript, and Dr D. W. Sutcliffe for editing the manuscript and supervising its conversion to the final book. The originals of the drawings by Professor Mizzaro-Wimmer are in her possession and she should be consulted before they are reproduced elsewhere. The work in England by U. H. Humpesch and in Austria by J. M. Elliott was supported jointly by the Austrian Academy of Sciences and The Royal Society through fellowships from the European Science Exchange Programme.

# REFERENCES

**Adamus, P. R. & Gaufin, A. R. (1976).** A synopsis of Nearctic taxa found in aquatic drift. *American Midland Naturalist*, **95**, 198-204.

**Allan, J. D. (1978).** Trout predation and the size composition of stream drift. *Limnology and Oceanography*, **23**, 1231-7.

**Allan, J. D. (1981).** Determinants of diet of brook trout (*Salvelinus fontinalis*) in a mountain stream. *Canadian Journal of Fisheries and Aquatic Sciences*, **38**, 184-92.

**Allan, J. D. (1983).** Predator-prey relationships in streams. *Stream Ecology: Application and Testing of General Ecological Theory* (ed. J. R. Barnes & G. W. Minshall), 191-229. Plenum Press, New York.

**Allan, J. D. (1984).** The size composition of invertebrate drift in a Rocky Mountain stream. *Oikos*, **43**, 68-76.

**Allan, J. D., Flecker, A. S. & McClintock, N. L. (1986).** Diel epibenthic activity of mayfly nymphs, and its nonconcordance with behavioural drift. *Limnology and Oceanography*, **31**, 1057-65.

**Allard, M. & Moreau, G. (1984).** Influence d'une acidification experimentale en milleu lotique sur la dérive des invertébrés benthiques. *Verhandlungen der Internationalen Vereinigung für theoretische und angewandte Limnologie*, **22**, 1793-1800.

**Andersen, T., Fjellheim, A., Larsen, R. & Otto, C. (1978).** Relative abundance and flight periods of Ephemeroptera, Plecoptera and Trichoptera in a regulated West Norwegian river. *Norwegian Journal of Entomology*, **25**, 139-44.

**Andrikovics, S. (1981).** Further data to the daily migration of the larvae of aquatic insects. *Opuscula zoologica. Budapest*, **17-18**, 49-55.

**Armitage, P. D. (1976).** A quantitative study of the invertebrate fauna of the River Tees below Cow Green Reservoir. *Freshwater Biology*, **6**, 229-40.

**Armitage, P. D., Furse, M. T. & Wright, J. F. (1985).** Further characters for distinguishing nymphs of the *Baetis vernus/tenax* group from *B. buceratus* Eaton (Ephem., Baetidae). *Entomologist's Monthly Magazine*, **121**, 235-7.

**Arnold, F. & Macan, T. T. (1969).** Studies on the fauna of a Shropshire hill stream. *Field Studies*, **3**, 159-84.

**Aro, J. E. (1928).** Suomen päiväkorennoiset. *Otavan Hyönteiskirjasiä*, **3**, 1-68.

**Aston, R. J., Sadler, K., Milner, A. G. P. & Lynam, S. (1985).** The effects of pH and related factors on stream invertebrates. *Central Electricity Generating Board, Research Laboratories Report*, TPRD/L/2792/N84, 8 pp.

**Badcock, R. M. (1949).** Studies in stream life in tributaries of the Welsh Dee. *Journal of Animal Ecology*, **18**, 193-208.

**Baekken, T. (1981).** Growth patterns and food habits of *Baetis rhodani*, *Capnia pygmaea* and *Diura nanseni* in a west Norwegian river. *Holarctic Ecology*, **4**, 139-44.

**Bailey, P. C. E. (1981).** Diel activity patterns in nymphs of an Australian mayfly *Atalophlebioides* sp. (Ephemeroptera:Leptophlebiidae). *Australian Journal of Marine and Freshwater Research*, **32,** 121-31.

**Baker, J. H. & Bradnam, L. A. (1976).** The role of bacteria in the nutrition of aquatic detritivores. *Oecologia*, **24,** 95-104.

**Bass, J. A. B. (1976).** Studies on *Ephemerella ignita* (Poda) in a chalk stream in S. England. *Hydrobiologia*, **49,** 117-21.

**Benech, V. (1972a).** Étude expérimentale de l'incubation des oeufs de *Baetis rhodani* Pictet. *Freshwater Biology*, **2,** 243-52.

**Benech, V. (1972b).** Le polyvoltinisme chez *Baetis rhodani* Pictet (Insecta, Ephemeroptera) dans un ruisseau a truites des Pyrenees-Atlantiques, le Lissuraga. *Annales d'Hydrobiologie*, **3,** 141-71.

**Bengtsson, B.-E. (1968).** Tillväxten hos nogra ephemerider i Ricklån. *Rapport Ricklån fältstation*, **15,** 1-22.

**Bengtsson, J. (1973).** Vaekst og livscyklus hos *Baetis rhodani* (Pict.) (Ephemeroptera). *Flora og Fauna*, **79,** 32-4.

**Besch, W. (1966).** Driftnetzmethode und biologische Fliesswassersuntersuchung. *Verhandlungen der Internationalen Vereinigung für theoretische und angewandte Limnologie*, **16,** 669-77.

**Bird, G. A. & Hynes, H. B. N. (1981a).** Movements of adult aquatic insects near streams in southern Ontario. *Hydrobiologia*, **77,** 65-9.

**Bird, G. A. & Hynes, H. B. N. (1981b).** Movement of immature aquatic insects in a lotic habitat. *Hydrobiologia*, **77,** 103-12.

**Bishop, J. E. (1969).** Light control of aquatic insect activity and drift. *Ecology*, **50,** 371-80.

**Bishop, J. E. & Hynes, H. B. N. (1969a).** Downstream drift of the invertebrate fauna in a stream ecosystem. *Archiv für Hydrobiologie*, **66,** 56-90.

**Bishop, J. E. & Hynes, H. B. N. (1969b).** Upstream movements of the benthic invertebrates in the Speed River, Ontario. *Journal of the Fisheries Research Board of Canada*, **26,** 279-98.

**Bisson, P. A. (1978).** Diel food selection by two sizes of rainbow trout (*Salmo gairdneri*) in an experimental stream. *Journal of the Fisheries Research Board of Canada*, **35,** 971-5.

**Blab, J., Nowak, E., Trautmann, W. & Sukopp, H. (1984).** *Rote List der gefährdeten Tiere und Pflanzen in der Bundesrepublik Deutschland.* Kilda-Verlag, Greven.

**Blair, K. G. (1929).** Two new British Mayflies (Ephemeroptera). *Entomologist's Monthly Magazine*, **65,** 253-5.

**Bogoescu, C. & Tabacaru, I. (1962).** Beiträge zur Kenntnis der Untersuchungsmerkmale zwischen den Gattungen *Ecdyonurus* und *Heptagenia* (Ephemeroptera). *Beiträge zur Entomologie*, **12,** 273-91.

**Bohle, H. W. (1969).** Untersuchungen über die Embryonalentwicklung und die embryonale Diapause bei *Baetis vernus* Curtis und *Baetis rhodani* Pictet (Baetidae, Ephemeroptera). *Zoologische Jahrbücher. Anatomie und Ontogenie der Tiere*, **86,** 493-575.

**Bohle, H. W. (1972).** Die Temperaturabhängigkeit der Embryogenese und der embryonalen Diapause von *Ephemerella ignita* (Poda) (Insecta, Ephemeroptera). *Oecologia*, **10**, 253-68.

**Bohle, H. W. (1978).** Beziehungen zwischen dem Nahrungsangebot, der Drift und der räumlichen Verteilung bei Larven von *Baëtis rhodani* (Pictet) (Ephemeroptera:Baëtidae). *Archiv für Hydrobiologie*, **84**, 500-25

**Bournaud, M., Maucet, D. & Chavanon, G. (1984).** Méthode pratique de mesure de la dérive des macroinvertébrés dans un cours d'eau application à la détection de perturbations du milieu. *Bulletin d'Ecologie*, **15**, 199-209.

**Bournaud, M. & Thibault, M. (1973).** La dérive des organismes dans les eaux courantes. *Annales d'Hydrobiologie*, **4**, 11-49.

**Bradbeer, P. A. & Savage, A. A. (1980).** Some observations on the distribution and life-history of *Caenis robusta* Eaton (Ephemeroptera) in Cheshire and North Shropshire, England. *Hydrobiologia*, **68**, 87-90.

**Bretschko, G. (1965).** Zur larvalentwicklung von *Cloeon dipterum, Cloeon simile, Centroptilum luteolum* und *Baetis rhodani. Zeitschrift für wissenschaftliche Zoologie*, **172**, 17-36.

**Bretschko, G. (1966).** Der Grüne bei Tragöss, Steiermark. Ein Beitragzur Karstlimnologie. *Internationale Revue der gesamten Hydrobiologie*, **51**, 699-726.

**Brittain, J. E. (1972).** The life cycles of *Leptophlebia vespertina* (L.) and *L. marginata* (L.) (Ephemeroptera) in Llyn Dinas, North Wales. *Freshwater Biology*, **2**, 271-7.

**Brittain, J. E. (1974).** Studies on the lentic Ephemeroptera and Plecoptera of southern Norway. *Norsk entomologisk tidsskrift*, **21**, 135-54.

**Brittain, J. E. (1976).** Experimental studies on nymphal growth in *Leptophlebia vespertina* (L.) (Ephemeroptera). *Freshwater Biology*, **6**, 445-9.

**Brittain, J. E. (1978).** The Ephemeroptera of Øvre Heimdalsvatn. *Holarctic Ecology*, **1**, 239-54.

**Brittain, J. E. (1979).** Emergence of Ephemeroptera from Øvre Heimdalsvatn, a Norwegian subalpine lake. *Proceedings of the 2nd International Conference on Ephemeroptera*, 115-24.

**Brittain, J. E. (1980).** Mayfly strategies in a Norwegian subalpine lake. *Advances in Ephemeroptera biology* (ed. J. F. Flannagan & K. E. Marshall), 179-86. Plenum Publishing Corporation, New York.

**Brittain, J. E. (1982).** Biology of mayflies. *Annual Review of Entomology*, **27**, 119-47.

**Brooker, M. P. & Edwards, R. W. (1974).** Effects of the herbicide paraquat on the ecology of a reservoir. III. Fauna and general discussion. *Freshwater Biology*, **4**, 311-35.

**Brooker, M. P. & Morris, D. L. (1978).** Production of two species of Ephemeroptera (*Ephemerella ignita* Poda and *Rhithrogena semicolorata* (Curtis)) in the upper reaches of the R. Wye, Wales. *Verhandlungen Internationale Vereinigung Limnologie*, **20**, 2600-4.

**Brown, D. S. (1960).** The ingestion and digestion of algae by *Chloeon dipterum* L. (Ephemeroptera). *Hydrobiologia*, **16,** 81-96.

**Brown, D. S. (1961a).** The food of larvae of *Chloeon dipterum* L. and *Baetis rhodani* Pictet (Insecta, Ephemeroptera). *Journal of Animal Ecology*, **30,** 55-75.

**Brown, D. S. (1961b).** The life-cycle of *Chloeon dipterum* L. (Ephemeroptera: Baetidae). *Entomologist*, **94,** 114-20.

**Brusven, M. A. & MacPhee, C. (1974).** An evaluation of squoxin on insect drift. *Transactions of the American Fisheries Society*, **103,** 362-5.

**Butz, I. (1979).** Strömungsverhalten von *Ecdyonurus venosus* (Fabr.) (Ephemeroptera). *Proceedings of the 2nd International Conference on Ephemeroptera*, 199-212.

**Campbell, R. N. B. (1985).** Comparison of the drift of live and dead *Baetis* nymphs in a weakening water current. *Hydrobiologia*, **126,** 229-36.

**Chaston, I. (1969).** Seasonal activity and feeding pattern of brown trout (*Salmo trutta*) in a Dartmoor stream in relation to availability of food. *Journal of the Fisheries Research Board of Canada*, **26,** 2165-71.

**Cianciara, S. (1979).** Life cycles of *Cloeon dipterum* (L.) in natural environment. *Polskie archiwum hydrobiologii*, **26,** 501-13.

**Cianciara, S. (1980).** Food preference of *Cloeon dipterum* (L.) larvae and dependence of their development and growth on the type of food. *Polskie archiwum hydrobiologii*, **27,** 143-60.

**Ciborowski, J. J. H. (1983).** Influence of current velocity, density, and detritus on drift of two mayfly species (Ephemeroptera). *Canadian Journal of Zoology*, **61,** 119-25.

**Ciborowski, J. J. H. & Corkum, L. D. (1980).** Importance of behaviour to the re-establishment of drifting Ephemeroptera. *Advances in Ephemeroptera biology* (ed. J. F. Flannagan & K. E. Marshall), 321-30. Plenum Publishing Corporation, New York.

**Ciborowski, J. J. H., Pointing, P. J. & Corkum, L. D. (1977).** The effect of current velocity and sediment on the drift of the mayfly *Ephemerella subvaria* McDunnough. *Freshwater Biology*, **7,** 567-72.

**Clifford, H. F. (1966).** The ecology of invertebrates in an intermittent stream. *Investigations of Indiana Lakes and Streams*, **7,** 57-98.

**Clifford, H. F. (1982).** Life cycles of mayflies (Ephemeroptera), with special reference to voltinism. *Quaestiones Entomologicae*, **18,** 15-90.

**Clifford, H. F., Hamilton, H. & Killins, B. A. (1979).** Biology of the mayfly *Leptophlebia cupida* (Say) (Ephemeroptera:Leptophlebiidae). *Canadian Journal of Zoology*, **57,** 1026-45.

**Corkum, L. D. (1978).** The influence of density and behavioural type on the active entry of two mayfly species (Ephemeroptera) into the water column. *Canadian Journal of Zoology*, **56,** 1201-6.

**Corkum, L. D. & Clifford, H. F. (1980).** The importance of species associations and substrate types to behavioural drift. *Advances in Ephemeroptera biology* (ed. J. F. Flannagan & K. E. Marshall), 331-41. Plenum Publishing Corporation, New York.

**Corkum, L. D. & Pointing, P. J. (1979).** Nymphal development of *Baetis vagans* McDunnough (Ephemeroptera:Baetidae) and drift habits of large nymphs. *Canadian Journal of Zoology*, **57**, 2348-54.

**Corkum, L. D., Pointing, P. J. & Ciborowski, J. J. H. (1977).** The influence of current velocity and substrate on the distribution and drift of two species of mayflies (Ephemeroptera). *Canadian Journal of Zoology*, **55**, 1970-7.

**Corrarino, C. A. & Brusven, M. A. (1983).** The effects of reduced stream discharge on insect drift and stranding of near shore insects. *Freshwater Invertebrate Biology*, **2**, 88-98.

**Coutant, C. C. (1964).** Insecticide Sevin: effect of aerial spraying on drift of stream insects. *Science*, **146**(3642), 420-1.

**Crisp, D. T. & Gledhill, T. (1970).** A quantitative description of the recovery of the bottom fauna in a muddy reach of a mill stream in southern England after draining and dredging. *Archiv für Hydrobiologie*, **67**, 502-41.

**Crowther, R. A. & Hynes, H. B. N. (1977).** The effect of road de-icing salt on the drift of stream benthos. *Environmental Pollution*, **14**, 113-26.

**Cummins, K. W. (1973).** Trophic relations of aquatic insects. *Annual Revue of Entomology*, **18**, 183-206.

**Dabrowski, K. & Glogowski, J. (1977).** Studies on the proteolytic enzymes of invertebrates constituting fish food. *Hydrobiologia*, **52**, 171-4.

**Décamps, H. & Elliott, J. M. (1972).** Influence de la mesure chimique du débit sur les invertébrés d'un ruisseau de montagne. *Annales de Limnologie*, **8**, 217-22.

**Degrange, C. (1959a).** L'ovolarviparité de *Cloëon dipterum* (L.) (Ephemeroptera:Baetidae). *Bulletin de la Société entomologique de France*, **64**, 94-100.

**Degrange, C. (1959b).** Nombre de mues et organe de Palmén de *Cloëon simile* Etn. (Éphéméroptères). *Compte rendu de l'Académie des sciences*, **249**, 2118-19.

**Degrange, C. (1960).** Recherches sur la reproduction des Éphéméroptères. *Travaux du Laboratoire de pisciculture de l'Université de Grenoble*, **50/51**, 7-193.

**Dejoux, C. & Elouard, J.-M. (1977).** Action de l'Abate sur les invertébrés aquatique cinétique de décrochement à court et moyen terme. *Cahiers de l'Office de la Recherche Scientifique et Technique Outre-Mer, Series Hydrobiologie*, **11**, 217-30.

**Dimond, J. B. (1967).** Evidence that drift of stream benthos is density related. *Ecology*, **48**, 855-7.

**Downing, J. A. & Rigler, F. H. (eds). (1984).** *A manual on methods for the assessment of secondary productivity in fresh waters. 2nd edition.* Blackwell Scientific Publications, Oxford.

**Edwards, R. W. & Brooker, M. P. (1982).** *The ecology of the Wye.* Junk, The Hague.

**Egglishaw, H. J. & Mackay, D. W. (1967).** A survey of the bottom fauna of streams in the Scottish Highlands. Part III. Seasonal changes in the fauna of three streams. *Hydrobiologia*, **30**, 305-34.

**Elliott, J. M. (1965a).** Daily fluctuations of drift invertebrates in a Dartmoor stream. *Nature, London*, **205**, 1127-9.

**Elliott, J. M. (1965b).** Invertebrate drift in a mountain stream in Norway. *Norsk entomologisk tidsskrift*, **13**, 97-9.

**Elliott, J. M. (1967a).** Invertebrate drift in a Dartmoor stream. *Archiv für Hydrobiologie*, **63**, 202-37.

**Elliott, J. M. (1967b).** The life histories and drifting of the Plecoptera and Ephemeroptera in a Dartmoor stream. *Journal of Animal Ecology*, **36**, 343-62.

**Elliott, J. M. (1967c).** The food of trout (*Salmo trutta*) in a Dartmoor stream. *Journal of Applied Ecology*, **4**, 59-71.

**Elliott, J. M. (1968).** The daily activity patterns of mayfly nymphs (Ephemeroptera). *Journal of Zoology*, **155**, 201-21.

**Elliott, J. M. (1969).** Diel periodicity in invertebrate drift and the effect of different sampling periods. *Oikos*, **20**, 524-8.

**Elliott, J. M. (1970a).** Methods of sampling invertebrate drift in running water. *Annales de Limnologie*, **6**, 133-59.

**Elliott, J. M. (1970b).** Diel changes in invertebrate drift and the food of trout *Salmo trutta* L. *Journal of Fish Biology*, **2**, 161-5.

**Elliott, J. M. (1971a).** Upstream movements of benthic invertebrates in a Lake District stream. *Journal of Animal Ecology*, **40**, 235-52.

**Elliott, J. M. (1971b).** The distances travelled by drifting invertebrates in a Lake District stream. *Oecologia*, **6**, 350-79.

**Elliott, J. M. (1972).** Effect of temperature on the time of hatching in *Baetis rhodani* (Ephemeroptera:Baetidae). *Oecologia*, **9**, 47-51.

**Elliott, J. M. (1973).** The food of brown and rainbow trout (*Salmo trutta* and *S. gairdneri*) in relation to the abundance of drifting invertebrates in a mountain stream. *Oecologia*, **12**, 329-47.

**Elliott, J. M. (1978).** Effect of temperature on the hatching time of eggs of *Ephemerella ignita* (Poda) (Ephemeroptera:Ephemerellidae). *Freshwater Biology*, **8**, 51-8.

**Elliott, J. M., Drake, C. M. & Tullett, P. A. (1980).** The choice of a suitable sampler for benthic macroinvertebrates in deep rivers. *Pollution Report of the Department of the Environment* No. 8, 36-44.

**Elliott, J. M. & Humpesch, U. H. (1983).** A key to the adults of the British Ephemeroptera with notes on their ecology. *Scientific Publications of the Freshwater Biological Association* No. 47, 101 pp.

**Elliott, J. M. & Minshall, G. W. (1968).** The invertebrate drift in the River Duddon, English Lake District. *Oikos*, **19**, 39-52.

**Elliott, J. M. & Tullett, P. A. (1978).** A bibliography of samplers for benthic invertebrates. *Occasional Publications of the Freshwater Biological Association* No. 4, 61 pp.

**Elliott, J. M. & Tullett, P. A. (1983).** A supplement to a bibliography of samplers for benthic invertebrates. *Occasional Publications of the Freshwater Biological Association* No. 20, 26 pp.

**Engblom, E. & Lingdell, P.-E. (1984).** The mapping of short-term acidification with the help of biological pH indicators. *Report of the Institute of Freshwater Research Drottningholm* No. 61, 60-8.

**Engblom, E., Lingdell, P. E. & Müller, K. (1981).** Occurrence and flight movements of mayflies (Ins. Ephemeroptera) in the mouth of a coastal stream in the northern Bothnian Sea. *Fauna Norrlandica*, **5**, 14 pp.

**Fahy, E. (1972).** The life cycles of some invertebrates in an isothermic stream in western Ireland. *Scientific Proceedings of the Royal Dublin Society*, **23**, 331-42.

**Fahy, E. (1973).** Observations on the growth of Ephemeroptera in fluctuating and constant temperature conditions. *Proceedings of the Royal Irish Academy, B*, **73**, 133-49.

**Fink, T. J. (1980).** A comparison of mayfly (Ephemeroptera) instar determination methods. *Advances in Ephemeroptera biology* (ed. J. F. Flannagan & K. E. Marshall), 367-380. Plenum Publishing Corporation, New York.

**Francissen, F. P. M. & Mol, A. W. M. (1984).** *Augerius Clutius and his 'De Hemerobio', an early work on Ephemeroptera*. Basilisken-Presse, Marburg.

**Froehlich, G. (1964).** The feeding apparatus of the nymph of *Arthroplea congener* Bengtsson (Ephemeroptera). *Opuscula Entomologica*, **29**, 188-208.

**Gledhill, T. (1959).** The life history of *Ameletus inopinatus* (Siphlonuridae, Ephemeroptera). *Hydrobiologia*, **14**, 85-9.

**Grandi, M. (1941).** Contribui allo studio degli Efemerotteri italiani. III. *Cloeon dipterum* L. *Bollettino dell-Istituto de entomolgia della R. Università degli studi di Bologna*, **13**, 29-71.

**Gyselman, E. C. (1980).** The mechanisms that maintain population stability of selected species of Ephemeroptera in a temperate stream. *Advances in Ephemeroptera biology* (ed. J. F. Flannagan & K. E. Marshall), 309-19. Plenum Publishing Corporation, New York.

**Hall, R. J., Pratt, J. M. & Likens, G. E. (1982).** Effects of experimental acidification on macroinvertebrate drift diversity in a mountain stream. *Water, Air, and Soil Pollution*, **18**, 273-87.

**Hall, R. J., Waters, T. F. & Cook, E. F. (1980).** The role of drift dispersal in production ecology of a stream mayfly. *Ecology*, **61**, 37-43.

**Haney, J. F., Beaulieu, T. R.** ***et al.*** **(1983).** Light intensity and relative light changes as factors regulating stream drift. *Archiv für Hydrobiologie*, **97**, 73-88.

**Harker, J. E. (1952).** A study of the life cycles and growth-rates of four species of mayflies. *Proceedings of the Royal Entomological Society of London (A)*, **27**, 77-85.

**Harker, J. E. (1953).** Migration of nymphs of *Ecdyonurus torrentis*. *Journal of Animal Ecology*, **22**, 418.

**Harriman, R. & Morrison, B. R. S. (1982).** Ecology of streams draining forested and non-forested catchments in an area of central Scotland subject to acid precipitation. *Hydrobiologia*, **88**, 251-63.

**Harrisson, C. M. H. (1958).** Some recent records of *Ephemera lineata* Eaton and *Potamanthus luteus* (L.) (Ephemeroptera). *Entomologist's Monthly Magazine*, **94**, 280.

**Hayden, W. & Clifford, H. F. (1974).** Seasonal movements of the mayfly *Leptophlebia cupida* (Say) in a brown-water stream of Alberta, Canada. *American Midland Naturalist*, **91**, 90-102.

**Hefti, D., Humpesch, U. H. & Tomka, I. (1988).** An electrophoretic and morphological study of three *Ecdyonurus* species (Ephemeroptera:Heptageniidae) occurring in the British Isles. *Systematic Entomology*, **13**, 161-70.

**Hellawell, J. M. (1978).** *Biological surveillance of rivers. A biological monitoring handbook*. Water Research Centre, Stevenage.

**Hellawell, J. M. (1986).** *Biological indicators of freshwater pollution and environmental management*. Elsevier, London.

**Hemsworth, R. J. & Brooker, M. P. (1979).** The rate of downstream displacement of macroinvertebrates in the upper Wye, Wales. *Holarctic Ecology*, **2**, 130-6.

**Hildebrand, S. G. (1974).** The relation of drift to benthos density and food level in an artificial stream. *Limnology and Oceanography*, **19**, 951-7.

**Hirvenoja, M. (1964).** Studien über die Wasserinsekten in Riihimäki (Südfinnland). IV: Ephemeroptera, Odonata, Hemiptera, Lepidoptera und Coleoptera. *Annales entomologici fennici*, **30**, 65-93.

**Holt, C. S. & Waters, T. F. (1967).** Effect of light intensity on the drift of stream invertebrates. *Ecology*, **48**, 225-34.

**Horst, T. J. (1976).** Population dynamics of the burrowing mayfly *Hexagenia limbata*. *Ecology*, **57**, 199-204.

**Hultin, L., Svensson, B. & Ulfstrand, S. (1969).** Upstream movements of insects in a South Swedish small stream. *Oikos*, **20**, 553-7.

**Humpesch, U. H. (1979).** Life cycles and growth rate of *Baetis* spp. (Ephemeroptera:Baetidae) in the laboratory and in two stony streams in Austria. *Freshwater Biology*, **9**, 467-79.

**Humpesch, U. H. (1980a).** Effect of temperature on the hatching time of eggs of five *Ecdyonurus* spp. (Ephemeroptera) from Austrian streams and English streams, rivers and lakes. *Journal of Animal Ecology*, **49**, 317-33.

**Humpesch, U. H. (1980b).** Effect of temperature on the hatching time of parthenogenetic eggs of five *Ecdyonurus* spp. and two *Rhithrogena* spp. (Ephemeroptera) from Austrian streams and English rivers and lakes. *Journal of Animal Ecology*, **49**, 927-37.

**Humpesch, U. H. (1981).** Effect of temperature on larval growth of *Ecdyonurus dispar* (Ephemeroptera:Heptageniidae) from two English lakes. *Freshwater Biology*, **11**, 441-57.

**Humpesch, U. H. (1982).** Effect of fluctuating temperature on the duration of embyronic development in two *Ecdyonurus* spp. and *Rhithrogena* cf. *hybrida* (Ephemeroptera) from Austrian streams. *Oecologia*, **55**, 285-8.

**Humpesch, U. H. & Elliott, J. M. (1980).** Effect of temperature on the hatching time of eggs of three *Rhithrogena* spp. (Ephemeroptera) from Austrian streams and an English stream and river. *Journal of Animal Ecology*, **49,** 643-61.

**Hynes, H. B. N. (1961).** The invertebrate fauna of a Welsh mountain stream. *Archiv für Hydrobiologie*, **57,** 344-88.

**Illies, J. (1952).** Die Mölle. Faunistisch-ökologische Untersuchungen an einem Forellenbach im Lipper Bergland. *Archiv für Hydrobiologie*, **46,** 424-612.

**Illies, J. (1968).** Ephemeroptera (Eintagsfliegen). *Handbuch der Zoologie*, **4,** (2), 1-63.

**Illies, J. (ed.) (1978).** *Limnofauna Europaea.* 2nd edn. Fischer, Stuttgart.

**Illies, J. & Masteller, E. C. (1977).** A possible explanation of emergence patterns of *Baetis vernus* Curtis (Ins: Ephemeroptera) on the Breitenbach-Schlitz studies on productivity, Nr. 22-. *Internationale Revue der gesamten Hydrobiologie*, **62,** 315-21.

**Jacob, U. (1974a).** Die bisher nachgewiesenen Ephemeropteren der Deutschen Demokratischen Republik. *Entomologisches Nachrichtenblatt*, **18,** 1-7.

**Jacob, U. (1974b).** Zur Kenntnis zweier *Oxycypha*-Arten Hermann Burmeisters (Ephemeroptera:Caenidae). *Reichenbachia*, **15,** 92-7.

**Jazdzewska, T. (1971).** Jetki (Ephemeroptera) rzeki Grabi. *Polskie pismo entomolgiczne*, **41,** 243-304.

**Jazdzewska, T. (1980).** Structure et fonctionnement des écosystèmes du Haut-Rhône français. 7. Le cycle vital d'*Ephemerella ignita* Poda 1761 (Ephemerellidae, Ephemeroptera) dans le Rhône lyonnais. *Bulletin d'Écologie*, **11,** 33-43.

**Jenkins, T. M., Feldmeth, C. R. & Elliott, G. V. (1970).** Feeding of rainbow trout (*Salmo gardneri*) in relation to abundance of drifting invertebrates in a mountain stream. *Journal of the Fisheries Research Board of Canada*, **27,** 2356-61.

**Jensen, C. F. (1956).** Ephemeroptera (Døgnfluer). En faunistisk biologisk undersøgelse of Skern Å. II. *Flora og Fauna*, **62,** 53-75.

**Johansson, K. & Nyberg, P. (1981).** Acidification of surface waters in Sweden – effects and extent 1980. *Institute of Freshwater Research, Drottningholm. Information Series* No. 6, 1-118.

**Jones, J. R. E. (1950).** A further ecological study of the River Rheidol: The food of the common insects of the main stream. *Journal of Animal Ecology*, **19,** 159-74.

**Keller, A. (1975).** The drift and its ecological significance. Experimental investigation on *Ecdyonurus venosus* (Fabr.) in a stream model. *Schweizerisch Zeitschrift für Hydrologie*, **37,** 294-331.

**Kjellberg, G. (1972).** Autecological studies of *Leptophlebia vespertina* (Ephemeroptera) in a small forest pool, 1966-1968. *Entomologisk tidskrift*, **93,** 1-29

**Kjellberg, G. (1973).** Growth of *Leptophlebia vespertina* L., *Cloeon dipterum* L. and *Ephemera vulgata* L. (Ephemeroptera) in a small woodland lake. *Entomologisk tidskrift*, **94,** 8-14.

**Klonowska, M. (1986).** The food of some mayfly (Ephemeroptera) nymphs from the streams of the Krakow-Czestochowa Jura (Southern Poland). *Acta hydrobiologica. Krakow*, **28**, 181-97.

**Kohler, S. L. (1983).** Positioning on substrates, positioning changes, and diel drift periodicities in mayflies. *Canadian Journal of Zoology*, **61**, 1362-8.

**Kohler, S. L. (1985).** Identification of stream drift mechanisms: an experimental and observational approach. *Ecology*, **66**, 1749-61.

**Landa, V. (1957).** Contribution to the distribution, systematics, development and ecology of *Habrophlebia fusca* (Curt.) *Habrophlebia lauta* McLachl. (Ephem.). *Acta Societatis entomologicae Czechosloveniae*, **54**, 148-56.

**Landa, V. (1968).** Developmental cycles of Central European Ephemeroptera and their interrelations. *Acta entomologica bohemoslovaca*, **65**, 276-84.

**Landa, V. (1969).** *Jepice – Ephemeroptera. Fauna CSSR*, 18. Praha. Academia.

**Langford, T. E. (1971).** The distribution, abundance and life-histories of stoneflies (Plecoptera) and mayflies (Ephemeroptera) in a British river, warmed by cooling-water from a power station. *Hydrobiologia*, **38**, 339-77.

**Langford, T. E. & Aston, R. J. (1972).** The ecology of some British rivers in relation to warmwater discharges from power stations. *Proceedings of the Royal Society of London (B)*, **180**, 407-19.

**Langford, T. E. & Bray, E. S. (1969).** The distribution of Plecoptera and Ephemeroptera in a lowland region of Britian (Lincolnshire). *Hydrobiologia*, **34**, 243-71.

**Larimore, R. N. (1974).** Stream drift as an indication of water quality. *Transactions of the American Fisheries Society*, **103**, 507-17.

**Larkin, P. A. & McKone, D. W. (1985).** An evaluation by field experiments of the McLay model of stream drift. *Canadian Journal of Fisheries and Aquatic Sciences*, **42**, 909-18.

**Larsen, R. (1968).** The life cycle of Ephemeroptera in the lower part of Aurland River in Sogn and Fjordane, Western Norway. *Norsk entomologisk tidsskrift*, **15**, 49-59.

**Larsen, R. (1978).** Fødens kvalitative betydning for veksten til *Baetis rhodani* Pikt. (Ephemeroptera). *Norwegian Journal of Entomology*, **25**, 106-8.

**Lavandier, P. (1982).** Evidence of upstream migration by female adults of *Baetis alpinus* Pict. (Ephemeroptera) at high altitude in the Pyrenees. *Annales de Limnologie*, **18**, 55-9.

**Lavandier, P. & Capblancq, J. (1975).** Influence des variations d'oxygene dissous sur les invertébrés benthiques d'un ruisseau des Pyrénées centrales. *Annales de Limnologie*, **11**, 101-6.

**Lavandier, P. & Dumas, J. (1971).** Cycles de developpement de quelques invertébrés benthiques dans des ruisseaux des Pyrénées Centrales. *Annales de Limnologie*, **7**, 157-72.

**Learner, M. A. & Potter, D. W. B. (1974).** The seasonal periodicity of emergence of insects from two ponds in Hertfordshire, England, with special reference to the Chironomidae (Diptera:Nematocera). *Hydrobiologia*, **44**, 495-510.

**Leivestad, H., Hendry, G., Muniz, I. P. & Snekvik, E. (1976).** Effects of acid precipitation on freshwater organisms. *Impact of acid precipitation on forest and freshwater ecosystems in Norway* (ed. F. H. Braekke), pp. 87-111. Research Report 6/76. SNSF Project, Oslo.

**Leland, H. V. (1985).** Drift response of aquatic insects to copper. *Verhandlungen der Internationalen Vereinigung für theoretische und angewandte Limnologie*, **22**, 2413-19.

**Levanidova, I. M. & Levanidov, V. Ya. (1965).** Sutochnye migratsii donnykh lichinok nasekomyskh v rechnoi strue. 1. Migratsii lichinok podenok v reke Khor. *Zoologicheskii zhurnal*, **44**, 373-85.

**Lichtenberg, R. (1973).** Die Entwicklung einiger charackteristischer Benthosorganismen des 'Hallateiches' südlich von Wien. *Annalen des naturhistorischen Museums in Wien*, **77**, 305-11.

**Lingdell, P.-E. & Müller, K. (1979).** Migrations of *Leptophlebia vespertina* L. and *L. marginata* L. (Ins: Ephemeroptera) in the estuary of a coastal stream. *Aquatic Insects*, **1**, 137-42.

**Macan, T. T. (1957).** The life histories and migrations of the Ephemeroptera in a stony stream. *Transactions of the Society for British Entomology*, **12**, 129-56.

**Macan, T. T. (1958).** Descriptions of the nymphs of the British species of *Heptagenia* and *Rhithrogena* (Ephem.). *Entomologist's Gazette*, **9**, 83-92.

**Macan, T. T. (1965).** The fauna in the vegetation of a moorland fishpond. *Archiv für Hydrobiologie*, **61**, 273-310.

**Macan, T. T. (1977).** A twenty-year study of the fauna in the vegetation of a moorland fishpond. *Archiv für Hydrobiologie*, **81**, 1-24.

**Macan, T. T. (1978).** Life histories of four species of Ephemeroptera. *Verhandlungen der Internationalen vereinigung für theoretische und angewandte Limnologie*, **20**, 2594-8.

**Macan, T. T. (1979).** A key to the nymphs of the British species of Ephemeroptera with notes on their ecology. *Scientific Publications of the Freshwater Biological Association* No. 20, 79 pp.

**Macan, T. T. (1981).** Life histories of some species of *Ecdyonurus* (Ephemeroptera) in the River Lune, north-western England. *Aquatic Insects*, **3**, 225-32.

**Macan, T. T. & Kitching, A. (1976).** The colonization of squares of plastic suspended in midwater. *Freshwater Biology*, **6**, 33-40.

**Macan, T. T. & Maudsley, R. (1968).** The insects of the stony substratum of Windermere. *Transactions of the Society for British Entomology*, **18**, 1-18.

**Mackey, A. P. (1978).** Emergence patterns of three species of *Caenis* Stephens (Ephemeroptera:Caenidae). *Hydrobiologia*, **58**, 277-80.

**Madsen, B. L. (1968).** A comparative ecological investigation of two related mayfly nymphs. *Hydrobiologia*, **31**, 337-49.

**Madsen, B. L., Bengtsson, J. & Butz, I. (1973).** Observations on upstream migration by imagines of some Plecoptera and Ephemeroptera. *Limnology and Oceanography*, **18**, 678-81.

**Madsen, B. L., Bengtsson, J. & Butz, I. (1977).** Upstream movement by some Ephemeroptera species. *Archiv für Hydrobiologie*, **81**, 119-27

**Maitland, P. S. (1965).** The distribution, life cycle, and predators of *Ephemerella ignita* (Poda) in the River Endrick, Scotland. *Oikos*, **16,** 48-57

**Malzacher, P. (1981).** Beitrag zur Insekten-faunistik Südwestdeutschlands: Ephemeroptera – Eintagsfliegen. *Mitteilungen*, **16,** 41-72

**Malzacher, P. (1984).** Die europäischen Arten der Gattung *Caenis* Stephens (Insecta: Ephemeroptera). *Stuttgarter Beiträge zur Naterkunde Serie A. (Biologie)* No. 373, 1-48.

**Malzacher, P. (1986).** Diagnostik, Verbreitung und Biologie der europäischen *Caenis*-Arten (Ephemeroptera:Caenidae). *Stuttgarter Beiträge zur Naturkunde Serie A (Biologie)* No. 387, 1-41.

**McArthur, J. V. & Barnes, J. R. (1985).** Patterns of macroinvertebrate colonization in an intermittent rocky mountain stream in Utah. *Great Basin Naturalist*, **45,** 117-23.

**McCafferty, W. P. & Edmunds, G. F. Jr (1979).** The higher classification of the Ephemeroptera and its evolutionary basis. *Annals of the Entomological Society of America*, **72,** 5-12.

**McClure, R. G. & Stewart, K. W. (1976).** Life cycle and production of the mayfly *Choroterpes (Neochoroterpes) mexicanus* Allen (Ephemeroptera:Leptophlebiidae). *Annals of the Entomological Society of America*, **69,** 134-44.

**McLay, C. (1970).** A theory concerning the distance travelled by animals entering the drift of a stream. *Journal of the Fisheries Research Board of Canada*, **27,** 359-70.

**Merritt, R. W. & Cummins, K. W. (1978).** *An introduction to the aquatic insects of North America*. 441 pp. Kendall/Hunt, Iowa.

**Metz, J.-P. (1974).** The invertebrate drift on the surface of a prealpine stream and its selective exploitation by rainbow trout (*Salmo gairdneri*). *Oecologia*, **14,** 247-67

**Minshall, G. W. & Winger, P. V. (1968).** The effect of reduction in stream flow on invertebrate drift. *Ecology*, **49,** 580-2.

**Mirjana, T. (1979).** Population dynamics of species of the genus *Baetis* Leach (Ephemeroptera) in the river Stavnja. *Godisnjak Biologškog instituta u Sarajevo*, **30,** 213-58.

**Mol, A. W. M. (1983).** *Caenis lactea* (Burmeister) in the Netherlands (Ephemeroptera:Caenidae). *Entomologische berichten*, **43,** 119-23.

**Mol, A. W. M. (1984).** The earliest epoch in the study of mayflies (Ephemeroptera); towards a reappraisal of the work of Augerius Cluteus. *Proceedings of the Fourth International Conference on Ephemeroptera* (ed. V. Landa, T. Soldan & M. Tonner), pp. 3-9. Czechoslovak Academy of Sciences, České Budějovice.

**Monk, D. C. (1976).** The distribution of cellulase in freshwater invertebrates of different feeding habits. *Freshwater Biology*, **6,** 471-5.

**Moon, H. P. (1938).** The growth of *Caenis horaria* (L.), *Leptophlebia vespertina* (L.) and *L. marginata* (L.) (Ephemeroptera). *Proceedings of the Zoological Society of London*, **108,** 507-12.

**Moon, H. P. (1940).** An investigation of the movements of freshwater invertebrate faunas. *Journal of Animal Ecology*, **9**, 76-83.

**Moore, J. W. (1977).** Some aspects of the feeding biology of benthic herbivores. *Hydrobiologia*, **53**, 139-46.

**Mottram, J. C. (1932).** The living drift of rivers. *Transactions of the Newbury District Field Club*, **6**, 195-8.

**Muirhead-Thomson, R. C. (1978).** Lethal and behavioral impact of chlorpyrifos methyl and temephos on select stream macroinvertebrates: experimental studies on downstream drift. *Archives of Environmental Contamination & Toxicology*, **7**, 139-47.

**Muirhead-Thomson, R. C. (1987).** *Pesticide impact on stream fauna with special reference to macroinvertebrates.* Cambridge University Press, Cambridge.

**Müller, K. (1954).** Investigations on the organic drift in North Swedish streams. *Report Institute of Freshwater Research, Drottningholm*, **35**, 133-48.

**Müller, K. (1963a).** Tag- Nachtrhythmus von Baetidenlarven in der Organischen Drift. *Naturwissenschaften*, **50**, 1-3.

**Müller, K. (1963b).** Diurnal rhythm in 'organic drift' of *Gammarus pulex. Nature*, **198**, 806-7.

**Müller, K. (1963c).** Temperatur und Tagesperiodik der 'Organischen Drift' von *Gammarus pulex. Naturwissenschaften*, **50**, 410-11.

**Müller, K. (1965).** Field experiments on periodicity of freshwater invertebrates. *Circadian Clocks* (ed. J. Aschof), pp. 314-17. Amsterdam.

**Müller, K. (1966).** Die Tagesperiodik von Fliesswasserorganismen. *Zeitschrift für Morphologie und Okologie der Tiere*, **56**, 93-142.

**Müller, K. (1970).** Tages- und Jahresperiodik der Drift in Fliessgewassern in verschiedenen geographischen Breiten. *Oikos*, Supplement, **13**, 21-44.

**Müller, K. (1973).** Circadian rhythms of locomotor activity in aquatic organisms in the subarctic summer. *Aquilo, Series Zoologica*, **14**, 1-18.

**Müller, K. (1974).** Stream drift as a chronobiological phenomenon in running water ecosystems. *Annual Review of Ecology and Systematics*, **5**, 309-23.

**Müller, K. (1982).** The colonization cycle of freshwater insects. *Oecologia*, **52**, 202-7.

**Müller-Liebenau, I. (1969).** Revision der europäischen Arten der Gattung *Baetis* Leach, 1815. (Insecta, Ephemeroptera). *Gewässer und Abwässer*, **48-49**, 1-214.

**Mundie, J. H. (1959).** The diurnal activity of the larger invertebrates at the surface of Lac La Ronge, Saskatchewan. *Canadian Journal of Zoology*, **37**, 945-56.

**Nagell, B. H. (1980).** Overwintering strategy of *Cloeon dipterum* L. larvae. *Advances in Ephemeroptera biology* (ed. J. F. Flannagan & K. E. Marshall), 259-64. Plenum, New York.

**Nagell, B. (1981).** Overwintering strategy of two closely related forms of *Cloeon* (*dipterum*?) (Ephemeroptera) from Sweden and England. *Freshwater Biology*, **11**, 237-44.

**Neave, F. (1930).** Migratory habits of the mayfly, *Blasturus cupidus*. *Ecology*, **11**, 568-76.

**Needham, P. R. (1928).** Net for capture of stream drift organisms. *Ecology*, **9**, 339-42.

**Neveu, A. & Échaubard, M. (1975).** The drift of aquatic and terrestrial invertebrates in a stream of Massif Central – the Couze Pavin. *Annales de Hydrobiology*, **6**, 1-26.

**Neveu, A., Lapchin, L. & Vignes, J. C. (1979).** Le macrobenthos de la basse Nivelle, petit fleuve côtier des Pyrénées-Atlantique. *Annales de Zoologie – Ecologie Animale*, **11**, 85-111.

**Nilssen, J. P. (1980).** Acidification of a small watershed in southern Norway and some characteristics of acidic aquatic environments. *Internationale Revue der gesameten Hydrobiologie*, **65**, 177-207.

**Obrdlik, P., Adámek, Z. & Zahrádka, J. (1979).** Mayfly fauna (Ephemeroptera) and the biology of the species *Potamanthus luteus* (L.) in a warmed stretch of the Oslava River. *Hydrobiologia*, **67**, 129-40.

**Olsson, T. & Soderstrom, O. (1978).** Springtime migration and growth of *Parameletus chelifer* (Ephemeroptera) in a temporary stream in northern Sweden. *Oikos*, **31**, 284-9.

**Ormerod, S. J. (1985).** The diets of breeding dippers *Cinclus cinclus* and their nestlings in the catchment of the River Wye, mid-Wales: a preliminary study by faecal analysis. *Ibis*, **127**, 316-31.

**Ormerod, S. J., Allinson, N., Hudson, D. & Tyler, S. J. (1986).** The distribution of breeding dippers (*Cinclus cinclus* (L.); Aves) in relation to stream acidity in upland Wales. *Freshwater Biology*, **16**, 501-7.

**Otto, C. & Sjostrom, P. (1986).** Behaviour of drifting insect larvae. *Hydrobiologia*, **131**, 77-86.

**Otto, C. & Svensson, B. S. (1981).** A comparison between food, feeding and growth of two mayflies, *Ephemera danica* and *Siphlonurus aestivalis* (Ephemeroptera) in a South Swedish stream. *Archiv für Hydrobiologie*, **91**, 341-50.

**Pearson, W. D. & Franklin, D. R. (1968).** Some factors affecting drift rates of *Baetis* and Simuliidae in a large river. *Ecology*, **49**, 75-81.

**Peckarsky, B. L. (1980).** Predator-prey interactions between stoneflies and mayflies: Behavioral observations. *Ecology*, **61**, 932-43.

**Pieczyński, E. (1964).** Analysis of numbers, activity and distribution of water mites (Hydracarina), and of some other invertebrates in the lake littoral and sublittoral. *Ekologia polska Series A*, **12**, 691-735.

**Pleskot, G. (1953).** Zur Okologie der Leptophlebiiden (Ephemeroptera). *Osterreichische zoologische Zeitschrift*, **4**, 45-107.

**Pleskot, G. (1958).** Die Periodizität einiger Ephemeropteren der Schwechat. *Wasser und Abwasser*, 1-32.

**Pleskot, G. (1961).** Die Periodizität der Ephemeropteren-fauna einiger österreichischer Fliessgewässer. *Verhandlungen der Internationalen vereinigung für theoretische und angewandte Limnologie*, **14**, 410-16.

**Ploskey, G. R. & Brown, A. V. (1980).** Downstream drift of the mayfly *Baetis flavistriga* as a passive phenomenon. *American Midland Naturalist*, **104**, 405-9.

**Poole, W. C. & Stewart, K. W.** (**1976**). The vertical distribution of macrobenthos within the Brazos River, Texas. *Hydrobiologia*, **50**, 151-60.

**Puthz, V.** (**1977**). Bemerkunden über europäische *Siphlonurus*-Arten (Insecta, Ephemeroptera). *Reichenbachia*, **16**, 169-75.

**Puthz, V.** (**1978**). Ephemeroptera. *Limnofauna Europaea*. (ed. J. Illies), pp. 256-63. Fischer, Stuttgart.

**Radford, D. S. & Hartland-Rowe, R.** (**1971**). A preliminary investigation of bottom fauna and invertebrate drift in an unregulated and a regulated stream in Alberta. *Journal of Applied Ecology*, **8**, 883-903.

**Rawlinson, R.** (**1939**). Studies on the life-history and breeding of *Ecdyonurus venosus* (Ephemeroptera). *Proceedings of the Zoological Society of London, Series B*, **109**, 377-450.

**Rosillon, D.** (**1986a**). Life cycle, growth, mortality and production of *Ephemerella major* Klapalek (Ephemeroptera) in a trout stream in Belgium. *Freshwater Biology*, **16**, 269-77.

**Rosillon, D.** (**1986b**). Life cycles of four ephemeropteran species in a chalky stream. *Polskie archiwum hydrobiologii*, **33**, 21-31.

**Russev, B.** (**1959**). Vol de compensation pour la ponte de *Palingenia longicauda* (Oliv.) (Ephem.) contre courant du Danube. *Compte rendu de l'Académie bulgare des sciences*, **12**, 165-8.

**Russev, B. K.** (**1973**). Kompensationsflug bei der Ordnung Ephemeroptera. *Proceedings of the 1st International Conference on Ephemeroptera* (ed. W. L. Peters & J. G. Peters), pp. 132-42. E. J. Brill, Leiden.

**Russev, B. K.** (**1987**). Ecology, life history and distribution of *Palingenia longicauda* (Olivier) (Ephemeroptera). *Tijdschrift voor Entomologie*, **130**, 109-27.

**Russev, B. K. & Doshkinova, M. G.** (**1985**). On the development and productivity of mayfly larvae (Ephemeroptera, Insecta) in a stretch of the Iskar River. *Hydrobiology*, **25**, 3-16.

**Sandrock, F.** (**1978**). A comparison of the insects emerging from two brooks in the region of Schlitz (Breitenbach and Rohrwiesenbach 1970-1971). *Archiv für Hydrobiologie (Supplementum)*, **54**, 328-408.

**Savage, A. A.** (**1986**). The distribution, life cycle and production of *Leptophlebia vespertina* (L.) (Ephemeroptera) in a lowland lake. *Hydrobiologia*, **133**, 3-19.

**Schmidt, H.** (**1951**). Amputation und Regeneration von Schwanffäen und Abdominalsegmenten bei Larven der Ephemeridenart *Cloeon dipterum* L. und ihr Einfluss auf das Hautungsintervall. *Zoologische Jahrbücher 56. Jena. Allgemeine Zoologie und Physiologie der Tiere*, **62**, 395-428.

**Schmidt, H.-H.** (**1984**). Einfluss der Temperatur auf die Entwicklung von *Baetis vernus* Curtis. *Archiv für Hydrobiologie, Supplementum*, **69**, 364-410.

**Schönmann, H.** (**1979**). Die Nahrungsaufnahme der Larven von *Siphlonurus aestivalis* Eaton. *Proceedings of the 32nd International Conference on Ephemeroptera*, 293-8.

**Sladeček, V.** (**1973**). System of water quality from the biological point of view. *Archiv für Hydrobiologie, Ergebnisse der Limnologie*, **7**, 1-218.

**Smock, L. A. (1980).** Relationships between body size and biomass of aquatic insects. *Freshwater Biology*, **10**, 375-83.

**Södergren, S. E. (1963).** Undersökningar av driftfaunan i Ricklean. *Laxforskningsinstitutet, Meddelande*, **5**, 1-24.

**Soderström, O. (1987).** Upstream movements of invertebrates in running waters – a review. *Archiv für Hydrobiologie*, **111**, 197-208.

**Soldán, T. (1979).** Struktur und Funktion der Maxillarpalpen von *Arthroplea congener* (Ephemeroptera, Heptageniidae). *Acta Entomologica Bohemoslovaca*, **76**, 300-7.

**Solem, J. O. (1973).** Diel rhythmic pattern of *Leptophlebia marginata* L. and *L. vespertina* L. (Ephemeroptera). *Aquilo, Series Zoologica*, **14**, 80-3.

**Sowa, R. (1965).** Ecological characteristics of the bottom fauna of the Wielka Puszcza stream. *Acta Hydrobiologica*, **7**, 61-92.

**Sowa, R. (1971).** Notes sur quelques *Rhithrogena* Eaton de la collection Esben-Petersen et la redescription de *Rhithrogena germanica* Eaton (Ephemeroptera, Heptageniidae). *Bulletin de l'Academie polonaise des sciences*, **19**, 485-92.

**Sowa, R. (1975a).** What is *Cloeon dipterum* (Linnaeus, 1761)? The nomenclatural and morphological analysis of a group of the European species of *Cloeon* Leach (Ephemerida:Baetidae). *Entomologica Scandinavica*, **6**, 215-23.

**Sowa, R. (1975b).** Notes on the European species of *Procloeon* Bengtsson with particular reference to *Procloeon bifidum* (Bengtsson) and *Procloeon ornatum* Tshernova (Ephemerida:Baetidae). *Entomologica Scandinavica*, **6**, 107-14.

**Sowa, R. (1975c).** Ecology and biogeography of mayflies (Ephemeroptera) of running waters in the Polish part of the Carpathians. 2. Life Cycles. *Acta Hydrobiologica*, **17**, 319-53.

**Sowa, R. (1979).** Le développement des Éphéméroptères de la rivière Dunajec aux environs de Piening. *Proceedings of the 2nd International Conference on Ephemeroptera*. 125-31.

**Statzner, B., Dejoux, C. & Elouard, J-M. (1984).** Field experiments on the relationship between drift and benthic densities of aquatic insects in tropical streams (Ivory Coast). 1. Introduction: review of drift literature, methods, and experimental conditions. *Revue d'Hydrobiologie tropicale*, **17**, 319-34.

**Statzner, B. & Mogel, R. (1985).** An example showing that drift net catches of stream mayflies (*Baetis* spp., Ephemeroptera, Insecta) do not increase during periods of higher substrate surface densities of the larvae. *Verhandlungen der Internationalen Vereinigung für theoretische und angewandte Limnologie*, **22**, 3238-43.

**Steine, I. (1972).** The number and size of drifting nymphs of Ephemeroptera, Chironomidae, and Simuliidae by day and night in River Stranda, Western Norway. *Norsk entomologisk tidsskrift*, **19**, 127-31.

**Strenger, A. (1953).** Zur Kopfmorphologie der Ephemeridenlarven. *Ecdyonurus* und *Rhithrogena*. *Österreichische zoologische Zeitschrift*, **4**, 191-228.

**Strenger, A. (1973).** Die Mandibelgestalt der Ephemeridenlarven als funktionsmorphologisches Problem. *Verhandlungsbericht der Deutschen Zoologischen Gesellschaft, 66. Jahresversammlung*,75-9.

**Strenger, A. (1975).** Zur Kopfmorphologie der Ephemeridenlarven *Ephemera danica*. *Zoologica*, **123**, 1-22.

**Strenger, A. (1979).** Die Ernährung der Ephemeropterenlarven als funktionsmorphologisches Problem. *Proceedings of the 2nd International Conference on Ephemeroptera*, 299-306.

**Sukop, I. (1973).** Annual cycle of mayflies (Ephemeroptera) in a karstic stream. *Acta Entomologica Bohemoslovaca*, **70**, 81-5.

**Sutcliffe, D. W. & Carrick, T. R. (1973).** Studies on mountain streams in the English Lake District. I. pH, calcium and the distribution of invertebrates in the River Duddon. *Freshwater Biology*, **3**, 437-62.

**Svensson, B. (1976).** The association between *Epoicocladius ephemerae* Kieffer (Diptera: Chironomidae) and *Ephemera danica* Müller (Ephemeroptera). *Archiv für Hydrobiologie*, **77**, 22-36.

**Svensson, B. (1977).** Life cycle, energy fluctuations and sexual differentiation in *Ephemera danica* (Ephemeroptera), a stream-living mayfly. *Oikos*, **29**, 78-86.

**Swain, R. & White, R. W. G (1985).** Influence of a metal-contaminated tributary on the invertebrate drift fauna of the King River (Tasmania, Australia). *Hydrobiologia*, **122**, 261-6.

**Tanaka, H. (1960).** On the daily change of the drifting of benthic animals in streams, especially on the types of daily change observed in taxonomic groups of insects. *Bulletin of the Freshwater Fisheries Research Laboratory, Tokyo*, **9**, 13-24.

**Thibault, M. (1969).** Le développement des Éphéméroptères semivoltins et univoltins d'un ruisseau de Pays Basque Français. Doctorat thèse. Université de Paris.

**Thibault, M. (1971).** Le developpement des Éphéméroptères d'un ruisseau a truites des Pyrénées-Atlantiques, le Lissuraga. *Annales de Limnologie*, **7**, 53-120.

**Thomas, A. G. B. (1975).** Éphéméroptères du Sud-Ouest de la France. I. – Migrations d'imagos à haute altitude. *Annales de Limnologie*, **11**, 47-66.

**Thorup, J. (1963).** Growth and life cycles of invertebrates from Danish springs. *Hydrobiologia*, **22**, 55-84.

**Thorup, J. (1973).** Interpretation of growth-curves for animals of running waters. *Verhandlungen der Internationalen vereinigung für theoretische und angewandte Limnologie*, **18**, 1512-20.

**Tokeshi, M. (1985).** Life-cycle and production of the burrowing mayfly, *Ephemera danica:* a new method for estimating degree-days for growth. *Journal of Animal Ecology*, **54**, 919-30.

**Townsend, C. R. & Hildrew, A. G. (1976).** Field experiments on the drifting, colonization and continuous redistribution of stream benthos. *Journal of Animal Ecology*, **45**, 759-72.

**Ulfstrand, S. (1968a).** Life cycles of benthic insects in Lapland streams (Ephemeroptera, Plecoptera, Trichoptera, Diptera Simuliidae). *Oikos*, **19**, 167-90.

**Ulfstrand, S. (1968b).** Benthic animal communities in Lapland streams. A field study with particular reference to Ephemeroptera, Plecoptera, Trichoptera and Diptera Simuliidae. *Oikos*, Supplement, **10,** 1-120.

**Ulfstrand, S. (1969).** Ephemeroptera and Plecoptera from River Vindelälven in Swedish Lapland. With a discussion of the significance of nutritional and competitive factors for the life cycles. *Entomologisk Tidskrift*, **90,** 145-65.

**Verrier, M-L. (1953).** Le rhéotropism des larves d'éphémères. *Bulletin biologique de la France et de la Belgique*, **87,** 1-34.

**Verrier, M.-L. (1956).** *Biologie des Éphémerès*. Armand Colin, Paris.

**Wallace, R. R. & Hynes, H. B. N. (1975).** The catastrophic drift of stream insects after treatments with methoxychlor (1,1,1-trichloro-2,2-bis(*p*-methoxy-phenyl) ethane.). *Environmental Pollution*, **8,** 255-68.

**Wallace, J. B. & Merritt, R. W. (1980).** Filter-feeding ecology of aquatic insects. *Annual Review of Entomology*, **25,** 103-32.

**Walton, O. E. (1980).** Active entry of stream benthic macroinvertebrates into the water column. *Hydrobiologia*, **74,** 129-39.

**Waters, T. F. (1961).** Standing crop and drift of stream bottom organisms. *Ecology*, **42,** 532-7.

**Waters, T. F. (1962).** Diurnal periodicity in the drift of stream invertebrates. *Ecology*, **43,** 316-20.

**Waters, T. F. (1965).** Interpretation of invertebrate drift in streams. *Ecology*, **46,** 327-34.

**Waters, T. F. (1966).** Production rate, population density, and drift of a stream invertebrate. *Ecology*, **47,** 595-604.

**Waters, T. F. (1969).** Invertebrate drift – ecology and significance to stream fishes. *Symposium of salmon and trout in streams*, 121-34. University of British Columbia, Vancouver.

**Waters, T. F. (1972).** The drift of stream insects. *Annual Review of Entomology*, **17,** 253-72.

**Waters, T. F. (1977).** Secondary production in inland waters. *Advances in Ecological Research*, **10,** 91-164.

**Wells, S. M., Pyle, R. M. & Colins, N. M. (1983).** *The IUCN Invertebrate Red Data Book*. IUCN, Gland.

**Welton, J. S., Ladle, M. & Bass, J. A. B. (1982).** Growth and production of five species of Ephemeroptera larvae from an experimental recirculating stream. *Freshwater Biology*, **12,** 103-22.

**Whelan, K. F. (1980).** Some aspects of the biology of *Ephemera danica* Müll. (Ephemeridae:Ephemeroptera) in Irish waters. *Advances in Ephemeroptera biology* (ed. J. F. Flannagan & K. E. Marshall), 187-99. Plenum, New York.

**Wiley, M. J. & Kohler, S. L. (1980).** Positioning changes of mayfly nymphs due to behavioral regulation of oxygen consumption. *Canadian Journal of Zoology*, **58,** 618-22.

**Wiley, M. J. & Kohler. S. L. (1984).** Behavioral adaptations of aquatic insects. *The ecology of aquatic insects* (ed. V. H. Resh & D. M. Rosenberg), pp. 101-33. Praeger, New York.

**Williams, D. D. (1980).** Invertebrate drift lost to the sea during low flow conditions in a small coastal stream in western Canada. *Hydrobiologia*, **75**, 251-4.

**Williams, D. D. (1981).** Migrations and distributions of stream benthos. *Perspectives in running water ecology* (ed. M. A. Lock & D. D. Williams), pp. 155-207. Plenum Press, New York.

**Williams, D. D. & Hynes, H. B. N. (1974).** The occurrence of benthos deep in the substratum of a stream. *Freshwater Biology*, **4**, 233-56.

**Williams, D. D. & Hynes, H. B. N. (1976).** The recolonization mechanisms of stream benthos. *Oikos*, **27**, 265-73.

**Wise, E. J. (1980).** Seasonal distribution and life histories of Ephemeroptera in a Northumbrian river. *Freshwater Biology*, **10**, 101-11.

**Wojtalik, T. A. & Waters, T. F. (1970).** Some effects of heated water on the drift of two species of stream invertebrates. *Transactions of the American Fisheries Society*, **99**, 782-7.

**Wright, J. F., Hiley, P. D. & Berrie, A. D. (1981).** A 9-year study of the life cycle of *Ephemera danica* Müll. (Ephemeridae:Ephemeroptera) in the River Lambourn, England. *Ecological Entomology*, **6**, 321-31.

**Zahrádka, J. (1978).** The production biology of two species of mayflies, *Potamanthus luteus* (Linné, 1767) and *Ephoron virgo* (Olivier, 1791). *Klub přír Brno*, **25**, 157-68.

**Zelinka, M. (1973).** Die Eintagsfliegen (Ephemeroptera) in Forellenbachen der Beskiden. II. – Produktion. *Hydrobiologia*, **42**, 13-19.

**Zelinka, M. (1977).** Production conditions of the polluted trout brook. *Folia Facultatis Scientiarum Naturalium Universitatis Purkynianae Brunensis, Biologia*, **18**, 7-105.

**Zelinka, M. (1980).** Differences in the production of mayfly larvae in partial habitats of a barbel stream. *Archiv für Hydrobiologie*, **90**, 284-97.

**Zelinka, M. (1984).** Production of several species of mayfly larvae. *Limnologica*, **15**, 21-41.

**Zelinka, M. & Marvan, P. (1976).** Notes to methods for estimating production of zoobenthos. *Folia Facultatis Scientiarum Naturalium Universitatis Purkynianae Brunensis, Biologia*, **17**, 5-55.

# INDEX

## A. SPECIES

Page numbers in bold type indicate main key references. Synonyms are shown in parentheses.

## B. FISHERMEN'S NAMES

## PUBLICATIONS OF THE FRESHWATER BIOLOGICAL ASSOCIATION

These publications and an up to date price list may be obtained direct from **Dept. DWS, Freshwater Biological Association, The Ferry House, Ambleside, Cumbria, LA22 0LP.**

## SCIENTIFIC PUBLICATIONS

5. A KEY TO THE BRITISH SPECIES OF FRESHWATER CLADOCERA, by the late D. J. Scourfield and J. P. Harding, 3rd ed., 1966. ISBN 0 900386 01 0
13. A KEY TO THE BRITISH FRESH- AND BRACKISH-WATER GASTROPODS, by T. T. Macan, 4th ed., 1977. ISBN 0 900386 30 4
16. A REVISED KEY TO THE BRITISH WATER BUGS (HEMIPTERA-HETEROPTERA), by T. T. Macan, 2nd ed., 1965. (Reprinted 1976) ISBN 0 900386 07 X
17. A KEY TO THE ADULTS AND NYMPHS OF THE BRITISH STONEFLIES (PLECOPTERA), by H. B. N. Hynes, 3rd ed., 1977. (Reprinted 1984). ISBN 0 900386 28 2
18. A KEY TO THE BRITISH FRESHWATER CYCLOPID AND CALANOID COPEPODS, by J. P. Harding and W. A. Smith, 2nd ed., 1974. ISBN 0 900386 20 7
23. A KEY TO THE BRITISH SPECIES OF FRESHWATER TRICLADS, by T. B. Reynoldson, 2nd ed., 1978. ISBN 0 900386 34 7
25. SOME METHODS FOR THE STATISTICAL ANALYSIS OF SAMPLES OF BENTHIC INVERTEBRATES, by J. M. Elliott, 2nd ed., 1977. ISBN 0 900386 29 0
27. A KEY TO BRITISH FRESHWATER FISHES, by Peter S. Maitland, 1972. ISBN 0 900386 18 5
29. TURBULENCE IN LAKES AND RIVERS, by I. R. Smith, 1975. ISBN 0 900386 21 5
30. AN ILLUSTRATED GUIDE TO AQUATIC AND WATER-BORNE HYPHOMYCETES (FUNGI IMPERFECTI), by C. T. Ingold, 1975. ISBN 0 900386 22 3
31. A KEY TO THE LARVAE, PUPAE AND ADULTS OF THE BRITISH DIXIDAE (DIPTERA), by R. H. L. Disney, 1975. ISBN 0 900386 23 1
32. A KEY TO BRITISH FRESHWATER CRUSTACEA MALACOSTRACA, by T. Gledhill, D. W. Sutcliffe and W. D. Williams, 1976. ISBN 0 900386 24 X
33. DEPTH CHARTS OF THE CUMBRIAN LAKES, by A. E. Ramsbottom, 1976. ISBN 0 900386 25 8
34. AN ILLUSTRATED KEY TO FRESHWATER AND SOIL AMOEBAE, by F. C. Page, 1976. ISBN 0 900386 26 6
35. A KEY TO THE LARVAE AND ADULTS OF BRITISH FRESHWATER MEGALOPTERA AND NEUROPTERA, by J. M. Elliott, 1977. ISBN 0 900386 27 4
37. A KEY TO THE ADULT MALES OF THE BRITISH CHIRONOMIDAE (DIPTERA), by L. C. V. Pinder, 1978. ISBN 0 900386 32 0